# GREAT STRUCTURES OF THE WORLD

By *H. Arthur Klein and Mina C. Klein*

SURF'S UP! *(An Anthology of Surfing)*

HYPOCRITICAL HELENA

MAX AND MORITZ

By *H. Arthur Klein*

GRAPHIC WORLDS OF PETER BRUEGEL THE ELDER

MASERS AND LASERS

BIOLUMINESCENCE

FUEL CELLS

SURFING

BY H. ARTHUR KLEIN AND MINA C. KLEIN

# GREAT STRUCTURES
# OF THE WORLD

THE WORLD PUBLISHING COMPANY

NEW YORK

*1337*

PUBLISHED BY The World Publishing Company
110 East 59th Street, New York, New York 10022
Published simultaneously in Canada by
Nelson, Foster & Scott Ltd.
Library of Congress catalog card number: 68-14699

*To Paulinchen, the greatest.*

# CONTENTS

## Contents

# NOTES ON ILLUSTRATIONS

*Frontispiece.* Facing title page. The Parthenon as it looked in Pericles' Athens

CHAPTER I.

*Page 17.* Photograph of a primitive (c. 3000 B.C.E.) wall painting from Tassili. From a private collection

*Page 22.* These prehistoric men were hunters and gatherers, living in temporary shelters made of branches and leaves.

CHAPTER II.

*Page 27.* The great ziggurat at Eridu was built about 4,270 years ago. Its lower levels still stand today. Wide World Photos

*Page 35.* Archaeologists who have carefully studied the remaining structure believe that the Ziggurat of Ur looked like this in the days of Nabon-idus. The drawing by Joseph Cellini of the Ziggurat of Ur is based on a reconstruction by E. Unger pictured in *Nineveh and Babylon* by André Parrot, London, 1958.

CHAPTER III.

*Page 41.* Detail of an engraving made after a painting by Pieter Bruegel the Elder depicting the biblical Tower of Babel. From the collection of Mr. and Mrs. Jake Zeitlin of Los Angeles

*Page 49.* The great tower rising in Babylon

CHAPTER IV.

*Page 51.* Photograph of the Pyramid of Khufu at Giza. A smaller pyramid is also shown, probably the Pyramid of Khafra. Arab Information Center

*Page 63.* Laborers erecting a step pyramid

CHAPTER V.

*Page 73.* Detail of the frieze of the Parthenon. British Museum

CHAPTER VI.

*Page 89.* Section of the Great Wall of China. From a private collection

*Page 100.* A guard at one of the many watch towers of the Great Wall in the time of Ch'in Shih Huang Ti

CHAPTER VII.

*Page 105.* Detail of the arches of the Colosseum as they look today. Italian Government Tourist Office

*Page 118.* Gladiators in the arena of the Flavian Amphitheater, now known as the Colosseum

CHAPTER VIII.

*Page 125.* View of the Church of Santa Sophia today. Turkish American Information and Tourist Office

*For their help in securing illustrative materials and for their gracious permission to reproduce these materials in this volume, the authors and The World Publishing Company wish to thank the persons and institutions named above.*

# FOREWORD AND ACKNOWLEDGMENTS

Fourteen great structures, groups of structures, or structural projects are presented here. They range far in location as well as in time. Each seems to the authors to have transcended its particular place or its immediate era and to have gained that broader significance implied in the word "great."

Emphasis is on the human meanings and the social impacts of these structures, not merely on physical bulk, area, or height; on their building materials, architecture, or ornamentation; or even on the abundance of human sweat, blood, and tears involved in their building in the first place.

We tried to select structures that represented in one way or another human dreams made real in stone or steel. Those dreams may be visions of delight, bitter reveries, or sheer nightmares. They may come from pasts vanished almost beyond recall, and from civilizations that have left little trace beyond such structural remains. On the other hand, other structures included are functioning parts of the world's present, and hold the promise of remaining so in its uncertain future.

Our title does not imply as invisible prefix *all* great structures of the world, or even *most* or *many*. It means, *some selected* great structures. The fourteen could have been increased to three or four times that many without exhausting the list of structures which we consider great in terms of people's beliefs, fears, hopes, memories, or aspirations. However, sheer bigness does not make books better or structures finer.

In our effort to find the human values behind the stones and to reach the social bases back of the rows of bricks or masses of concrete and steel, we have been helped by information, material, and kind attention from several people whom it is a welcome privilege to thank here.

These include, for the section on "The Parthenon of the Acropolis, Athens—Greek Glory on a Hilltop," Mr. Malcolm Parker, Director, The Parthenon in Centennial Park at Nashville, Tennessee, that extraordinary full-size replica built between 1920 and 1931. Also Mr. J. W. Graham, Research Curator of the Greek and Roman Department of the Royal Ontario Museum, University of Toronto, Toronto, Canada, custodian of the fine scale model of the Acropolis as a whole, made by the American architect-archaeologist G. P. Stevens.

They include, for the section on "The Empire State Building: Mammoth of Manhattan," Mr. Jack L. Friedman of the Ray Josephs organization, also of Manhattan. For the section on "The Grand Coulee Dam: Greatest Structure of Man-Made Stone," Mrs. Lee Proschka, Acting Administrative Assistant, Columbia Basin Project, Bureau of Reclamation, U. S. Department of Interior, Ephrata, Washington.

For the section on "The Netherlands Reclamation Projects: Land Won from the Sea," Mr. H. F. van den Broek, Director, Netherlands Information Service (Western Division), San Francisco, California; Mr. H. Menke, Consulate General of The Netherlands, and staff, Los Angeles; Professor Dr. Sjoerd Groenman, Institute of Sociology of the Rijksuniversiteit, Utrecht, The Netherlands; and the office of the Noordoostpolderwerken, Zwolle, The Netherlands.

And finally, for the section on "The United Nations Buildings: Staff Headquarters for Peace," the UN Office of Public Information.

Several other persons aided with information and ideas on undoubtedly great structures that could not be included within these covers. These individuals remain unmentioned in print here, though not privately unthanked.

Once again we express a gratitude that does not diminish with repetition to aiders and abettors in the Los Angeles County Library system: Mrs. Deborah B. Wilds, regional librarian; Mr. James G. Gear, reference librarian; as well as Mrs. Jill McGrew and Mr. Tony

Dorn of the Bookmobile that brings so much helpful material. Likewise the ever friendly and helpful staff of the admirable Library system of UCLA headed by Dr. Robert Vosper. All have been generous in permitting access to the treasures they care for and share.

For any outright errors or "controversial" interpretations in the text, the authors alone must assume responsibility as they do for the choices of structures included as well as the difficult and often painful associated task of omitting the others. The word is omitting, not "rejecting," however; and if readers ask, "Wouldn't it have been a good idea to include Great Structure X, and even Y?" the answer certainly would have to be a hearty "Yes!"

Perhaps the future will bring opportunity to make suitable amends to some of those omitted structures whose unique greatness cannot be denied.

— H. Arthur Klein and Mina C. Klein

# GREAT STRUCTURES OF THE WORLD

# I

## PREHISTORY

## MAN'S MARCH TO GREAT STRUCTURES

Then the dance, the song, the story,
Or the hours given over to dreaming,
Once having so marched.

— CARL SANDBURG, *The People, Yes*

The great structures selected in this book were planned and built during many different periods of time. The earliest among them date from the days of prehistory—that is, from the dim eras before written records. Yet, in a broader sense, they are all rather recent when compared with the duration of man's presence on this earth. The structures great enough to survive in fact or in historical records have all originated within the past ten or twelve thousand years. The human species, however, has been present on earth perhaps four or five million years!

Great structures have been built only during the latest tiny fraction of the total time that men have been residents of this planet. This fact in itself gives a great deal of information about the relationship between mankind and the great structures that men have built.

Human beings were never solitary or isolated dwellers at any stage of man's presence on earth. From the first, our ancient ancestors lived, hunted, gathered food, defended themselves, and traveled in groups—bands, tribes, or great families.

Millions of years ago these basically social beings became makers and users of simple tools. They used stones for hammers and missiles, and sticks for clubs, spears, levers, or props. From the animals they were able to kill for food, they took bones and teeth to use as tools, and skins and sinews for other uses. The tools they developed and put to work became continually more effective.

The most careful diggings, siftings, and study of remains in many parts of the world have not disclosed any great and enduring structures that we can feel certain were completed more than ten thousand years ago. This is striking, for in the world with which we Americans are familiar, progress, growth, and technical advance are associated with enormous constructions of many kinds: road systems, bridges, canals, dams, factories, skyscrapers, public and educational institutions, warehouses, terminals, and others.

The ability of men to build big and impressive structures has in fact far outstripped the ability they have shown for building security and abundance for all within a nation—and peace and fruitful cooperation between nations.

While some relatively small segments of the world's present population are surrounded now by more material things than men ever had within reach before, great numbers of their fellow men on earth remain at the ragged edge of starvation and desperation.

Amid such sharp and ever sharpening contrasts, the hope for spreading plenty to all of mankind and securing peace lies in directions that may seem to have little connection with the great structures of past and present. Yet when we examine some of the wonders of modern physical construction for peaceful purposes, can we doubt that a time which commands such vast powers over nature could also banish the old curses of famine, poverty, ignorance, and misery?

Such a world of shared plenty and secured peace could be the greatest of all structures—not a fabrication of stone and steel, but a society in which the wonders of science and the well-being of abundance are common wherever men live and labor. The aims and ambitions that bring change into the world are made of such dreams—dreams that cannot be disregarded or gainsaid.

## TIES BETWEEN SOCIETIES AND THEIR STRUCTURES

Close connections have always existed between the ways human groups lived and the kinds of structures they built for themselves or their rulers.

During the first several million years that men existed on earth, they had to solve one basic problem before they could undertake anything else: How to keep alive until tomorrow?

Small tribal groups or great "families" were fully engaged in the daily struggle to find, catch, or steal enough to eat, and to escape the menaces that surrounded them. They constructed only temporary shelters, moved along when necessary to new areas where they might fare better, and carried with them only bare essentials.

The efforts of every active, healthy member of the group were needed just to feed and shelter the group as a whole. And so by day and night they sought nuts, fruits, seeds, shellfish, or edible animals that could be caught or trapped. They learned to use the sun and, later, fire to prepare food that was not good when eaten raw. They learned to find shelter and safety from bitter cold, blasting wind, drenching downpours, blinding sun, or savage beasts.

They learned how to shape more effective clubs and axes and later how to project small spears that we call arrows. And what they learned they shared and transmitted by means of the patterns of signals that we call speech.

Such basic problems had to be answered every day by actions. These were the absorbing essentials of human existence during the vast eras and stages that archaeologists and anthropologists call by such names as the paleolithic and the mesolithic human cultures. These were the long ages before men had effectively mastered the cultivation of food plants (agriculture) and the domestication of useful animals such as sheep, goats, pigs, cattle, horses.

The latest of the three great prehistoric cultural stages is called the neolithic culture. The *neo* in that name signifies "new." What was new and revolutionary was, first, the far greater efficiency of agriculture and, second, domestication of suitable animals.

We often talk today of "making a living." Only since the dawn of this relatively recent epoch of the neolithic culture have men truly been able to "make" their livings on earth. During the millions of years preceding, they had to "take" their livings somehow amid a nature whose course they could not influence effectively, let alone control.

Since the dawn of the neolithic stage, important and increasing groups of men attained effective skills in manipulating their environment and, as a result, they could remain rooted in suitable surround-

ings instead of constantly wandering on to where the pickings or the huntings might be better. They then truly began to "make" their own living, and the resulting changes in their ways of life changed them, their thinking, their aims, and their relationships with each other. Change was now the order of the day.

All the enormous and accelerating changes wrought by mankind since the neolithic revolution have been accomplished in about ten or twelve thousand years. Not more than about half that revolutionary period is "historic." The earlier half lies before written and symbolic records were kept. Hence, it must be reconstructed with the help of objects and fragments dug from the soil.

Carl Sandburg wrote beautifully of the great transformations in human life and attitude that became possible with the changes we have outlined:

> Once having marched
> Over the margins of animal necessity,
> Over the grim line of sheer subsistence
> Then man came
> To the deeper rituals of his bones,
> To the lights lighter than any bones,
> To the time for thinking things over,
> Then the dance, the song, the story,
> Or the hours given over to dreaming,
> Once having so marched.

—FROM *The People, Yes*

Man also came finally to the time of building substantial, large, and lasting structures. That stage came only, and could come only, after the development of stable, dependable, and productive agriculture. It was stable because the group did not have to move on every few years as the soil became depleted. It was dependable since the new farmers knew what to plant, how to tend it, and how to harvest and use the final crop. It was productive: the results of one man's labor fed not only himself but possibly many others.

It was in this way that certain particular groups of people, within a few centuries after they became settled farmers, had evolved new methods of making a living from the land. This new life led to extraordinary consequences: food reserves and, sometimes, surpluses; growing populations; larger settlements becoming towns and cities; the appearance of social classes and the growth of conflicts between such classes. All these far-reaching and significant innovations in human history led before long to the first of the great structures that we shall seek to recapture from the mists of the past.

## CROSSING THE LINE

The relics found and interpreted by archaeologists indicate that "the grim line of sheer subsistence" began to be passed in a significant way by about the year 8000 B.C.E. (Before the Christian Era). Human relics known to be older than those are remains of wandering hunters and gatherers of wild food. However, by about that date there were groups of humans residing in small, settled communities, and engaging in the systematic production of their own food. They were the pioneers of agriculture.

But this far-reaching change did not take place everywhere at once. In fact, the evidence seems strong that primitive farmers appeared in western Asia at least one thousand years before such farmers appeared further west, in Egypt, or in the lands around the Levant and around the Aegean Sea.

Everywhere else in the Old World (eastern hemisphere) and in the New World (western), this epoch-making change in the ways men worked and lived came about later still. The neolithic stage spread, apparently, from region to region, and we cannot assign to it any one date unless we are careful to make clear just what part of the world we have in mind.

Western Asia is now the recognized cradleland for this enormous innovation in human living and human social structure. By the time these changes had reached what is now western Europe to the west and China to the east, three or four thousand years had elapsed. It appears that there were western Asian cities in existence whose techniques were based on the use of fine bronze tools and utensils before western Europe's first farmers began to plant their crops and care for their meager herds and flocks!

Two particular regions in western Asia were involved in this great new way of living. One is at the eastern end of the Mediterranean Sea. Formerly called Palestine, it includes the present nations of Israel and Jordan. The other region, in present-day Iraq, we shall consider later under the name of "Mesopotamia."

In the Israel-Jordan region, between 8000 and 7000 B.C.E., arose the early mesolithic culture called the *Natufian*. It was a real transition between two ways of life. The Natufian people were primarily hunters but had begun to harvest certain useful grasses—in other words, to gather grain.

At the site of the later city of Jericho, now in western Jordan, is an oasis that lies hundreds of feet below the level of the sea. Here, archaeologists have found precious clues to the past in a multiple-level mound, called a *tell*. It appears that the people of the Natufian culture, still using stone tools, had established a kind of shrine at the spring in this oasis by about 7800 B.C.E. This period is indicated by the ultra-modern atomic time-measuring method known as radiocarbon or Carbon–14 dating.

At higher levels in this *tell* lie other later clues. They show that by about eight centuries later, around 7000 B.C.E., the Natufians had begun to live in frail, temporary huts during most of the year. They had either become settled farmers by that time or farmers who still hunted in a supplementary way when they could take the time from working the land.

The Natufian remains have parallels elsewhere in western Asia. If we make a leap on the map to the southern shores of the Caspian Sea in present-day Iran, we come to the region of the Hotu and Belt caves where remains have been found indicating a similar story of transition to neolithic ways of life. Other significant sites are those of Jarmo, Sarab, and Guran in the Zagros mountains of Iran, and Tepe Sabz and Ali Kosh in the southwestern part of that nation.

What do these first known neolithic sites have in common? They are located on what must have been the best farming land in regions where agriculture could be carried on without the aid of artificial irrigation. The villages or settlements seem to have been small, their total population numbering up to three hundred people. Their crude shelters were clumped close together within a land area usually no larger than one or two acres.

Here were, so far as we can judge now, the world's first true farmers. They had begun their plantings with two primitive forms of grain—a two-row barley and a crude kind of wheat called *emmer*. Their animals were apparently limited to some barely tame offspring of wild sheep and goats.

By the period between 5500 and 5000 B.C.E. a complete pattern of agricultural economy had emerged. It was based on hybrid cereal plants with far higher yields than the first barley and emmer, and on flocks of fully domesticated sheep, goats, pigs, and cattle. Furthermore, by this time, these early farmers had learned how to work land when natural rainfall was lacking. At the Sabz site in Iran traces of systematic irrigation dating back to about 5500 B.C.E. have been found.

Improved production meant greater abundance of food, and that in turn made population growth possible. By about 5000 B.C.E. in favored farming regions of western Asia, the villages were sometimes placed close enough so that one could be seen from the other. No village seemed to have been more distant from its nearest neighbor than a comfortable day's walk.

The new production methods meant that land areas which would have been almost useless to the old hunting cultures now became possible and even desirable sites for the expanding agricultural populations. The trend was thus downward from the hilly country toward more flat and fertile soils.

And so we follow our early ancestors into that second and especially significant section of western Asia, the history-rich sector known through long centuries as the land between the two rivers: Tigris and Euphrates. The Greek name that so long marked it, *Mesopotamia*, means "between the rivers."

It was here that history itself and the first great structures began.

# II

## THE ZIGGURATS

---

## TOWERS OF MESOPOTAMIAN MUD

Now that Ziggurat had become old. On the
ancient foundations . . . I rebuilt the ziggurat
as it was in olden times, with mortar and
burnt bricks. . . .

— AN INSCRIPTION OF NABON-IDUS

The land between the two rivers where human history began is part of "the fertile crescent." We are concerned here with that area of the crescent that lies in what is now Iraq. A map of the world should show the two rivers clearly. Both rivers flow in a southeasterly direction—the Euphrates in the west, the Tigris in the east. They flow out of hilly regions where wandering tribes of early hunters pursued their prey, or searched for edible plants when hunting was poor. Then the rivers draw together and merge into a single stream that empties into the Persian Gulf. The general direction of this flow could be indicated by a line drawn through the fabled city of Baghdad toward that Gulf.

The waters of the Tigris and Euphrates were heavy with the rich sediments which they carried down from the upland regions. Periodically these streams flooded their banks and deposited layers of this rich silt on the surrounding land. From this was formed through the ages the great alluvial plain of southern Mesopotamia— the region that came to be known as Sumer. Further north lay the neighboring and related region called Akkad (or Accad).

Each year the sediment renewed the fertility of the flat, sun-baked plain through which their waters flowed. It was a region fit for productive farming of abundant cereals, fruits, and livestock—provided men could solve the problems of flood control, drainage of saturated land, and irrigation during the long, rainless seasons.

The soil of ancient Sumer has thus far revealed relatively few relics of human handiwork that can be positively dated earlier than about 3000 B.C.E. Yet what has been found led to a most important conclusion: in this hot alluvial plain of the two rivers were built the world's first large towns and cities—including great structures whose renown long outlasted them. These buildings inspired the most fabulous and famous of all stories of men's efforts to build great structures—the biblical story of the Tower of Babel.

## NEW SOCIETIES IN SUMER AND AKKAD

The first farming groups that learned to master the fertile Mesopotamian land slowly and steadily expanded their control and enlarged their numbers. The towns and cities, the towers and temples that finally appeared in Mesopotamia earlier than elsewhere were no sudden innovations. They were the outcome of gradual growth. The changes that made them possible had to do not only with irrigation and land drainage but also with the way these people lived and worked. The patterns of social relationship and control that emerged were quite different from those that had existed during the long ages when tribes of equals cooperated in hunting, fishing, or gathering of wild foods.

A word used to define these new, complex, and distinctive patterns is "civilization." The world's first civilizations appeared in this fertile land between the two rivers. The evidences of civilization in Mesopotamia definitely predate those in the land that clung to the river Nile—Egypt.

One structure in particular marked the sites of the first civilized communities in Sumer. It was the multistory, stepped-back tower topped by a shrine to the local god or gods.

The first origins of these Mesopotamian towers were modest enough. Because the soil of Sumer was often soggy or saturated with water, the earliest residents learned to build mounds or platforms to support their crude clay shelters, their storerooms, and the altars on which they made offerings to the gods to grant good harvests and increase of flocks.

The sequences of generations and centuries brought greater mastery in control of the land and the waters for irrigation. Populations grew. The projects to drain land and to channel flood waters grew too. People worked in larger groups on more extensive tasks.

Leadership and centralization of authority became more pronounced.

These changes were reflected indirectly in the growth of their shrine structures: they became larger and taller. What had been essentially a table on a platform became a shrine on top of a tower. Or perhaps on top of a series of towers that grew in the process of rebuilding and improving older towers whose mud bricks had deteriorated from long exposure.

Finally the primitive Sumerian shrine had grown into the typical Mesopotamian tower, whose image we find magnified and satirized in the story of the Tower of Babel. The shrine on top was no longer open to all who dwelt on the land roundabout. It had become a secret and sacred place. The common workers were not admitted to it. It was reserved now for a group that previously had not existed apart from the people. These were the priests, professionals of religion and ritual. They, with their staffs and servants, administered the tower shrine, the temple beside it, and much of the land around, which was owned by the god but managed by the priests as his representatives on earth.

## SIGNIFICANT FINDS FROM OLD SUMER

Shrine remnants dating back to about 5300 B.C.E. have been found at Abu Sharein on the Euphrates. This is the site of the ancient town of Eridu. Archaeologists found a layer of fish bones on that temple altar. At the time this altar was in use, the waters of the Persian Gulf extended inland to Eridu. The people there were fishermen-farmers, just as the early Natufians had been hunter-farmers. The bones apparently were the remains of sacrifices offered in the hope of attaining good catches in the future.

Eridu's early mixed culture moved toward effective agriculture. By about 4000 B.C.E. people of the Eridu culture were gathered in towns composed of houses made from the bricked clay of the land itself. These groups of residences extended over areas as large as four or five acres.

The people of such early towns worked together. They formed drainage ditches to reclaim swampy land for farming. They made and tended irrigation ditches to bring water to the fields in the dry seasons. And they erected even more imposing shrines for their worship.

The Eridu culture gave way in time to a more advanced culture, called the Ubaid, after the site of a series of important excavations. The Ubaid peoples built rectangular, raised platforms on which they placed the tables for their religious offerings.

By 3500 B.C.E., as shown by excavations at Warka, a large walled city had been built. This is the site whose ancient name was Uruk, given in the Bible also in the form of Erech. The early city of Uruk certainly contained a prominent temple and a stepped tower topped by a shrine.

By this time the city had a centralized shrine in the charge of full-time priests whose influence grew even greater.

Centuries of change must be compressed into a few sentences here. Leonard Woolley, a leading archaeologist in the study of Sumerian sites, has noted that every temple owned "more or less extensive" tracts of farmland. The produce from such land was either the outright property of the god, or else was paid in part as a tithe to the temple priesthood. Thus wealth and worship became fused. The tower and the temple were the outward symbols. The effective control, however, lay with the priestly group. Worshipers brought them offerings in kind— animals, fruits, sometimes precious metals.

Less than five miles from Uruk is the site now called Muquayyar (or Muquaiyir). It was once the great center called Ur. Here are the remains of the best preserved of all the Mesopotamian tower-shrines, some thirty of which have been found in Iraq. This impressive ruin is called *the Ziggurat of Ur*.

*Ziggurat* (pronounced zig′-oo-rat′) is derived from a word that meant "height." Sometimes the same word is spelled *zikkurat* or *ziqqurat*. Thus the Sumerians and their successors in the land between the two rivers called their typical towers "the high place" or simply "the height." The idea of loftiness was important to these dwellers on very level lands.

## FROM TEMPLE RECORDS TO WRITING

Discoveries at Ur and elsewhere reveal a complex and often astounding pattern of life. The affairs of the local god "had to be run on business lines," as Leonard Woolley put it. There were the tithes and tributes to collect, the crop yields to be recorded, the crop shares to be received and stored until needed. There were craftsmen to whom raw materials were turned over to be worked for the temple and the priests. There was all the management of the lands owned outright by the temple and worked by its serfs.

The need for record-keeping spurred invention. Marks made in tablets of moist clay became the first such records. The marks became simplified and turned into symbols. Thus between 3500 and 3000 B.C.E. began the system of symbols that evolved into writing. The wedge-shaped marks made by a stylus in clay tablets and cylinders created the form of writing called *cuneiform*. These hardened records of Mesopotamian origin have been found by the thousands. Scholars learned to decipher them. Thus great doors were opened to knowledge of this earliest adventure in civilization.

Based on these clay records, we can say that by 2500 B.C.E. the new "civilized" structure of life was firmly established on that inter-river plain. It was based on a greater productivity than men had ever attained before. The rivers, brown with their burden of rich mud, flowed through broad, well-irrigated fields planted with well-tended barley, wheat, groves of date-palms, olives, figs, and grapes. Rich pastureland abounded. Herds of cattle, sheep, and goats grazed or rested and were constantly tended.

This labor was done by bands of hard-working Sumerians, descendants of the hunters-turned-farmers who once had learned step by step how to plant, cultivate, and harvest. Yet now the land these people worked was not theirs. Neither were the herds they tended. The abundance and the luxury flowed, in one way or another, either to the city's temple complex or to its palaces. The temple meant the priests, their officers, and administrators. The palaces meant the king, his nobles, military officers, and men-at-arms. The workers in the fields, orchards, and workshops received food, clothing, and shelter sufficient for their bare family needs and for the periodic festivals and holidays.

Their labor was carefully watched by stewards and overseers. Collection of tithes and taxes was well organized. Behind the tax-collectors stood the power of the city-state—the magistrates, officers, and soldiers. Torture or even death threatened those who refused to pay. This situation has been summarized by Leonard Cottrell, author of many books on archaeological discoveries: "The bulk of the people are probably less free and independent than their ancestors, but the community as a whole is richer. This is known as civilization."[1]

Closer study shows that the riches of civilization were not shared throughout the "community as a whole." The social structure in Sumer and later civilizations of the region resembled their towers—broad at the bottom, small at the top. The vast majority of people were now workers without land or wealth. Only a small proportion lived in relative luxury and power at the pinnacle.

## BUILDING MATERIALS OF THE ZIGGURATS

The best preserved of all ziggurats, that of Ur, was a solid mass of bricks, from inside to outside. Its base was about 200 by 150 feet, and it rose to a height of some 70 feet. This called for a large number of bricks, all handmade from the clay soil.

Two kinds of bricks were used. Simple sun-dried bricks, forming the inner core of the tower, were surrounded by a thick jacket of fired or burnt bricks, eight feet thick. Burning bricks made them stronger, more durable, more resistant to time.

The Ziggurat of Ur shows how the architects and engineers of that region learned to deal with problems in construction. The raw or unburnt bricks forming the core were likely to swell if they became water-soaked. Thus downpours of rains or floods around the base could burst the walls of the tower itself. To prevent this, the walls were pierced at intervals with drainage ducts, some-

times called "weeper holes." These allowed excess interior moisture to flow out safely.

Next was the matter of the mortar. The use of asphalt or bitumen was well-established in this oil-rich land between the two rivers. Deposits of pitch, or crude petroleum, were easily found in the nearby desert. These were evidences of the "black gold" that has brought vast wealth to many rulers and owners in that part of the world in modern times.

In the great Ziggurat of Ur, the "mortar" was also bitumen or pitch. It not only helped to hold the bricks together but also gave added protection against the great enemy—moisture.

## THE HISTORY OF THE ZIGGURAT OF UR

Let us travel in imagination through the centuries to show how prolonged and repeated was the building of impressive ziggurat towers by the monarchs of the Mesopotamian region. Such an excursion must resemble a hop, skip, and jump progression rather than a pilgrimage, for we have time and space here only to touch the highlights.

About 2350 B.C.E. the great King Sargon reigned in Akkad near what was to be known much later by the name of Babylon. Sargon achieved renown as a builder of imposing towers and temples to the gods of his regime.

About 250 years later, we find a ruler with the significant name of Ur-Nammu, monarch of the dynasty of Ur. That name means much to everyone familiar with the first books of the Old Testament of the Bible which tells that Abraham, the great patriarch of all Israel, came originally from the Mesopotamian region called "Ur of the Chaldees."

This King ruled from about 2113 to 2096 B.C.E. Inscriptions from a much later date indicate that during his reign a great ziggurat was built, but not completed. Then Dungi, son of Ur-Nammu, came to the throne and completed the tower, known usually as the *Ziggurat of Ur*.

We pause next about two centuries later when we find a dominant city-state with the familiar name of Babylon. On its throne is a monarch whose name has become familiar as one of the first important law-givers of history: King Hammur-abi, often written simply as Hammurabi.

The evidence indicates that not only was substantial building done in his era, but by that time careful state supervision was being given to the construction of public monuments, such as ziggurats and temples, or of private residences and other structures. The Code of Hammurabi, a set of surviving laws identified with his name, includes the oldest known "building regulations." It provided heavy punishments for Babylonian contractors and masterbuilders whose constructions collapsed and caused death or serious damage to innocent occupants or neighbors!

It is clear that by the time of Hammur-abi the techniques and styles of construction were established and systematized so that standards of strength and survival could be set and enforced by the dread power of the central government. A Babylonian citizen who ordered a new house built or an old one repaired, no less than a monarch who ordered a tower or temple or palace, had the right to expect that it would be well-built. If the finished structure proved defective, the costs and the punishments fell on the responsible builder!

Our final leap through time in Mesopotamia brings us to the very last native monarch of that amazing region of successive civilizations and city-states. He was King Nabon-idus (or Nabonidus) father of the unfortunate Prince Bel-shazzar (or Belshazzar), whose ill-timed feasting and final defeat by the invading Persians in 539 B.C.E. has been commemorated by poets, composers, and artists.

Before that Persian victory, however, Nabon-idus ruled in splendor. He lived up to the prerogatives and the practices of previous ambitious kings of that region by ziggurat-building to glorify and perpetuate his name. He rebuilt the famed Ziggurat of Ur in honor of Nannar, the Babylonian moon-god. Within that tower by his order were placed clay cylinders whose cuneiform inscriptions were to make his name and fame immortal. Though they were forgotten or neglected during intervening ages, they are now well known. Nabon-idus and his ironical fate are famous again, thanks to modern archaeology.

Let us listen to the voice of this vanished monarch addressing us through these records of baked clay, enveloped in the tower:

> "Nabon-idus king of Babylon, am I the reverent worshiper of the great gods. The Ziggurat . . . in Ur, which Ur-Nammu, a king before me, had built but not completed . . . Dungi, his son, finished it. I saw [this] on the inscription of Ur-Nammu and his son Dungi. . . ."

Thus our reading of the inscription of Ur-Nammu reveals that his knowledge of preceding ziggurat builders had come similarly from his reading of their ancient surviving inscriptions. Then Nabon-idus continues to pay tribute to his own achievements:

> "Now that Ziggurat [in Ur] had become old. On the ancient foundations . . . I rebuilt the ziggurat as it was in olden times, with mortar and burnt bricks. . . ."

The inscription concludes by offering prayers for the lives and good fortunes of both King Nabon-idus and his son, Prince Belshazzar. One cannot resist recalling that even as these inscriptions were being scratched into the damp clay cylinders, the forces of the new Persian power were gathering, training, and preparing for the final attack which would overthrow this last native empire in the land which was once known as Sumer between the two historic rivers, Tigris and Euphrates.

That attack, carried out with almost surprising swiftness in 539 B.C.E. by the Persian forces under Cyrus, brought the total defeat of King Ur-Nammu and as an act of Persian revenge, the execution of his son, the crown prince Bel-shazzar, who had commanded the Babylonian defense forces. Thus Cyrus placed himself on the throne of Babylon and ended the dynasty of the Neo-Babylonian or Chaldean kings, who had included, among others, the famous and mighty monarch Nebu-chadnezzar II (605–652 B.C.E.).

This final defeat of native Mesopotamian rulers by the then little-known, new forces from the Persian lands, suggests that once again behind the outward façade of pomp and power of a Mesopotamian empire there was a weak social foundation.

In this significant sector of the earth's surface, we have seen that there rose and fell a long series of "civilized" city-states based on relatively advanced agricultural techniques, marked socially by sharp class distinctions and subordinations of large groups of working people to small numbers of rulers, military men, and professional priests; and marked outwardly, above all else, by the appearance, repair, renewal, and replacement of the striking ziggurats.

Almost every important dynasty and individual ruler of this Mesopotamian region during some three thousand years of intrigue, conquest, and power was to a greater or lesser extent a ziggurat builder. These structures were thus symbols of authority and eminence, as well as of religious ritual and centralized observance.

The ziggurats do not, like some temples or tombs of Egypt and elsewhere, preserve heroic statues of the rulers who ordered them built or the priests who administered them. Nevertheless, as we reconstruct the forces at work in those thousands of years in the land between the two famous rivers, we are reminded of the unforgettable and ironical poem *Ozymandias* written by Percy Bysshe Shelley.

> I met a traveller from an antique land
> Who said: "Two vast and trunkless legs of stone
> Stand in the desert. Near them, on the sand,
> Half sunk, a shattered visage lies, whose frown,
> And wrinkled lip, and sneer of cold command,
> Tell that its sculptor well those passions read
> Which yet survive, stamped on these lifeless things,
> The hand that mocked them and the heart that fed.
> And on the pedestal these words appear—
> "My name is Ozymandias, king of kings:
> Look on my works, ye Mighty, and despair!"
> Nothing beside remains. Round the decay
> Of that colossal wreck, boundless and bare
> The lone and level sands stretch far away.

In the region that the Greeks named Mesopotamia many a comparable record has been exhumed from the lone and level sands, or has been inferred from the state of the ruins of what was once a proud tower or arrogant defense wall. And from this region and its characteristic towers arose the story of the most famous tower that was intended to climb to Heaven itself, the fabulous structure known as *The Tower of Babel*.

# III

## THE TOWER OF BABEL

---

## THE TOWER THAT WAS TO BE TALLEST

Then they said to one another, "Come, let us build ourselves
a tower whose top shall reach to the heavens, thus making
a great name for ourselves, so that we may not be scattered
all over the earth."

—*The Bible*

The story of man's most ambitious or over-ambitious attempt at great construction appears in the Bible. It does not mention the word "ziggurat." And it is known to millions by the familiar name of *The Tower of Babel.*

Scholars agree that the roots of this brief and dramatic story lie in the ziggurats of Mesopotamia, and there is little doubt that it was inspired by one or more of three ziggurats whose locations are known today.

By tracing the story of the Tower of Babel we may shed unexpected light on these early great structures of the land between the Tigris and Euphrates. The story appears in the opening book, Genesis, of the Old Testament following the narrative of the great Flood and its aftermath.

The Ark bearing Noah, his family, and all the animals, has finally landed safely on the Ararat mountains. The occupants of the Ark have gone out into the world, once again to live and labor on the land which is now dry.

We are told that Noah's descendants included the ancestors of the population that occupied the land between the two rivers. Noah had a son named Ham, who had a son, Cush, who had a son named Nimrod, "a mighty hunter." Nimrod founded a kingdom that began with "Babel and Erech and Accad and Calneh in the land of Shinar." Some of these names should already be familiar. Erech was the Bible's name for Uruk; Accad and Akkad are identical; and Shinar stood for the entire region that historians often call Sumer or Sumeria. Babel is the biblical name for Babylon.

The Babel Tower tale is given here in the modern English language rather than the English of the time of King James in the

43

seventeenth century. In order to attain the greatest clarity, several translations have been consulted, two of which were completed within the past thirty years. The result may give new insight into the story that is usually told in the stately and somewhat archaic language of the King James version.

This then is the Tale of the Tower of Babel, of how different languages appeared on earth, and why they have since seemed to divide and to separate men:

> At this time the whole earth used but a single language, which had few words.
>
> During a movement of people from the east, men found a plain in the land of Shinar and settled there.
>
> Then they said to one another, "Come, let us make bricks, burning them well."
>
> So they used bricks for stones and asphalt for mortar.
>
> Then they said to one another, "Come, let us build ourselves a tower whose top shall reach to the heavens, thus making a great name for ourselves, so that we may not be scattered all over the earth."
>
> Then the Lord came down to look at the city and the tower that the human beings had built.
>
> The Lord said, "They are just one single people, and they all speak the same language. If this is what they are able to do as a start, then nothing else that they decide to do will prove impossible for them. Come, let us go down and there make such a babble of their language that they will not understand one another's speech."
>
> In this way the Lord scattered them from there all over the wide earth, and they had to give up building the city.
>
> That is why its name is called *Babel* because it was there that the Lord made a *babble* of the languages of the entire earth, and there that the Lord scattered men all over the wide earth.

Though it is brief, or perhaps partly because it is so brief, this simple, vivid narrative is full of fascinating points. Some of them are well worth short explanations here.

The similar sound of the name "Babel" and the word "babble" is clear. It forms a pun in which different senses are tied together by similar sounds. This pun in English is a reflection of a very similar pun in the original Hebrew, the language in which the story was first written. The Hebrew word root *balal* means "to confuse" or "to bewilder." This sounded much like the name Babil or Babel which meant Babylon, accounting for the final sentence which equates Babel with the babble or confusion of languages that from then on afflicted man all over the earth.

Babel had no such significance in the languages of the peoples of Mesopotamia, however. It meant "the gates of Heaven" in their language.

The tale tries to answer serious and continuing problems. How did the divisions and conflicts come between men on earth? Why can men not understand each other, since they are all descendants of the same family?

As in many other legends or allegories, the blame is placed here on excessive human ambition and arrogance. The implied moral is that "pride goes before a fall." The great structure that would have reached to the heavens becomes the occasion for a punishment that prevents mankind from realizing even the first essential of communal life on earth—understanding and harmonious co-existence.

## THE APPEARANCE OF THE FIRST
## TOWER OF BABEL STORY

When did the Tower of Babel story first appear? We can give very probable guesses but no positive proofs. From the style and vocabulary of the Hebrew in which it is written, leading scholars conclude that it was set down in the southern Jewish kingdom of Judah, whose capital was Jerusalem.

The time of that first composition cannot be assigned to one decade or perhaps even to one century. It must have been, however, after the death of King Solomon (about 930 to 920 B.C.E.) but it was certainly earlier than 750 B.C.E.

The Tower of Babel story is one of the parts of the book of Genesis that has been traced to a so-called "J document." This is not an actual physical manuscript or writing, such as the famous Dead Sea Scrolls. It is the name given to the unknown original of those sections in which the name for God is represented by the four Hebrew consonants that stand for *YHWH*. Since the vowels were not indicated in Hebrew writing, scholars have had to guess at what they must have been. This led in the past to the English word "Jehovah." Today, scholars believe that the original must have sounded more like "Yahweh."

It is the J of Jehovah that led to the label of the J document. It is contrasted with another narrative, in which the deity is called Elohim, and which is believed to derive from a supposed "E document."

The Tower of Babel story, in its own uncertain history, illustrates some of the confusions of language, history, and human records. In brief, it can be considered a vivid and dramatic anecdote that appeared first between the middle of the tenth century and the eighth century B.C.E., and was later edited into its present form, but not later than the middle of the fourth century B.C.E. It is old indeed, but it does not lack interesting information about how ziggurats were built in Mesopotamia.

A distance of 700 or 800 miles separated Jerusalem, capital of Judah, from the site of Babylon on the Euphrates River. Travelers and merchants from Babylon to Jerusalem must have carried word about the striking towers rising above the sun-drenched plain between the two rivers.

FINDING THE REAL TOWER OF BABEL

In attempts to identify the original Tower of Babel, scholars and archaeologists generally agree in reducing the candidates to just three among the thirty or forty ziggurats whose sites are now known.

(1) The ziggurat that stood within the city of Babylon, four miles north of the small town of Hilleh, is most prominently mentioned as the probable inspiration for the tower in the Bible story.

(2) Others suggest the ziggurat whose ruins can still be seen at nearby Birs Nimrud, on the site once known as Borsippa, ten miles southwest of the Babylonian ruins.

(3) A third nominee for this historical honor is the ziggurat whose remains stand at the site of ancient Dur-Kurigalzu near Baghdad, about fifty miles north of Hilleh. The modern name for this site is spelled in many ways—sometimes Akerkuf, or Aqurquf, or even Aqur Quf.

The remains of the ziggurats of Borsippa and Dur-Kurigalzu have resisted the inroads of thousands of years. They are ruins, but impressive ruins. Onlookers could easily imagine their past splendors. As travelers, including Bible students and archaeologists, began to visit each ruin, natives living nearby assured them with pride that this was indeed the famed Babel Tower of the Bible.

The ziggurat of Babylon, however, had vanished utterly. It was demolished, like the rest of that proud city that once ruled all the Near East. Even its mud bricks had been removed and used for small residences in nearby villages that survived. It is no wonder that the Babylon ziggurat received little attention for a long time.

Just after the start of the seventeenth century, John Cartwright visited the land between the two rivers. He was taken to the ruins of the ziggurat at Akerkuf, towering nearly 190 feet above the plain, and assured by his guides that here were the remains of the Tower of Babel that King Nimrod had once begun to build. Other travelers gazed in awe at the ziggurat ruins of Birs Nimrud, and returned to tell their audiences at home that they had beheld the authentic Babel Tower of the Bible.

It may well be that all three ziggurats helped to shape the biblical tale of the tower. Time, however, has swallowed up most of what we would like to know about the Babylonian tower's size, shape, and other special characteristics. Scholars and artists have cooperated to make pictures of how it probably looked in the days of its glory. Though these are conjectures, there is no doubt that it was famous and much admired.

## BABYLON'S HOUSE OF THE FOUNDATIONS
## OF HEAVEN AND EARTH

Like other great ziggurats in the Mesopotamian region, the Babylonian tower had its own special name. It was called *E-temen-anki*, meaning "House of the Foundations of Heaven and Earth." Its setting suggested its importance. A large walled court, about 1500 square feet in area, surrounded it. It stood beside the Euphrates with the Temple of Marduk, not as lofty but extensive, nearby. Close to these religious structures was a great enclave containing the priests'

residences, offices, storerooms, workshops, treasuries, quarters for the administrative staff, harems for their wives, and so on.

Like other great cities of those ages, Babylon was ringed by high defense walls. This city's walls were especially tall for the times, but the shrine at the top of E-temen-anki could be seen above them. Approaching travelers, merchants, and workers could glimpse its summit shining in the sun.

How high was it? Will Durant wrote that the tower's seven stages of gleaming enamel crowned by the shrine rose "to a height of 650 feet."[2] That impressive figure, however, is almost certainly too much. The most reliable estimates suggest that its height was not over 300 feet, and that its base or bottom level was a square, just under 300 feet on a side. Andre Parrot, a French archaeologist who supports this estimate, believes that it may have been the tallest structure in Babylonian civilization.

Its construction was typical of the traditional ziggurats of the historic land of the Tigris and Euphrates rivers. The interior core consisted of sun-dried mud bricks. For greater strength and improved internal drainage of moisture, layers of reed matting were inserted at intervals between the courses of brick inside the tower.

The exterior jacket was formed from fired bricks. Delightful to the eye was the outermost layer, fired and enameled in vivid colors and laid in lively geometrical designs.

Is there a surviving description of this ziggurat by any contemporary person who gazed on it in admiration, awe, or possibly jealousy? There is indeed a brief but well-known description written by Herodotus (485–425 B.C.E.), the famous Greek traveler, historian, and collector of gossip. We cannot be certain that Herodotus actually saw the ziggurat of Babylon. In fact, there is good reason to believe that he did see the ziggurat of Borsippa but talked with people who actually had seen the tower of Babylon.

In 539 B.C.E. Nabon-idus, the last native king of Babylon was overthrown by the forces of King Cyrus of Persia. Babylon then became a vassal state of the new conquerors, part of the so-called Achaemenian Empire, governed from Susa and Ecbatana—the centers now known respectively as Sushan and Hamadan.

The Babylonian subjects began to rebel against their overlords during the reign of the Achaemenian King Xerxes I. This so infuriated Xerxes that in 484 B.C.E. he ordered the extinction of the separate "Kingdom of Babel" in his empire.

Part of this extermination included the removal of the golden statue of the Babylonian god, Marduk. This was quite likely the traditional image that had been worshiped in the ziggurat shrine or the nearby temple. A Babylonian priest who tried to prevent removal of the statue was slain. Systematic destruction of the ziggurat and other great structures of Babylon followed. If this did happen, then the ziggurat must have been a mere ruin by the time Herodotus was a child and a mere memory by the time he could have traveled to Babylon.

It seems likely that Herodotus was told about E-temen-anki by people who had seen it.

> ". . . a tower of solid masonry, upon which was raised a second tower, and on that a third, and so on up to eight. The ascent to the top is on the outside by a path which winds around all the towers. When one is about half way up, one finds a resting place and seats, where people commonly sit some time on their way up to the summit. On the topmost tower is a spacious temple, and inside the temple stands a couch of unusual size, richly ornamented, and with a golden table by its side."

Finally, in a delightful commentary characteristic of his chatty style, Herodotus betrays that all or most of the foregoing facts may have been based on hearsay—and that there were limits to what a skeptical Greek would believe from Mesopotamian sources:

> "They also declare—but I for my part do not believe it—that the god comes down in person into this chamber and sleeps upon the couch."

Babylon itself has long been dust and mud. Where once stood the ziggurat named for the foundations of heaven and earth, is now a mere miserable swamp beside the Euphrates. Yet thanks to the living imagination of men the fame of the Tower of Babylon has resounded for thousands of years.

# IV

## THE PYRAMIDS OF EGYPT

## STONE MOUNTAINS
## THAT MOCKED AT TIME

Time mocks at all things, but the pyramids mock at time. . . .

— ARABIC PROVERB

The next of the world's great structures lie along a single river, the Nile, westward and a little south of the ziggurats in the land of the twin rivers, Tigris and Euphrates. These are the pyramids of Egypt, now called the United Arab Republic.

From the ziggurat sites in western Asia to the pyramid sites in northeast Africa is a short journey in our age of swift air travel. In the days when ziggurats and pyramids were first constructed, however, such a journey could require many weeks of difficult, even dangerous, travel. In spite of this fact, convincing clues indicate that important influences passed from the one to the other, probably along early trade routes.

As early as 7000 B.C.E. small tribal groups were already settled, planting cereal grains and beginning with animal domestication, in areas now within Israel, Jordan, Iraq, and Iran. In the Nile valley comparable techniques were not attained until one or even two thousand years later.

More important, it seems that when these new, more productive methods did rise in Egypt they had been inspired by the example of the pioneers of western Asia. Thus the first suitable seed grains, especially barley and wheat, appear to have been carried westward to the narrow fertile zone along the Nile. Egypt's first domesticated livestock seem to have come by the same route. And it is possible to trace westward movement of important artifacts—tools and utensils, and even structures.

The last stage before recorded history began in Egypt is sometimes called the *Gerzean* culture. Gerzean pottery and tools show kinship to artifacts found to the east. Rather close influences most likely linked the early Egyptians with peoples living then in such eastward areas as the Sinai peninsula and present-day Israel and Jordan.

These movements of things and methods resulted largely from the movements of people. Within Egypt itself such movements carried populations from Lower Egypt in the north around the Nile delta, to Upper Egypt further south.

Populated Egypt was confined closely to strips along the Nile. The width of land suitable for farming was not more than ten to fifteen miles from the riverbanks. Hills and mountain ridges limited this unusual valley on both sides. Beyond the mountains to the west lay the Libyan and Sahara Deserts and beyond the eastern range, the banks of the Red Sea.

Rain is almost unknown in Egypt. Yet the land is not barren within this favored fertile zone. Each year the great Nile overflows its banks. It spreads over the valley a rich layer of organic slime. These floods begin about mid-July and continue into September. Then the waters recede. By January, when the Nile is safely within its banks again, seed can be sown and cultivated with expectation of good yields.

Such fertilizing floods could also damage or ruin man-made structures. Hence the tribes who first became settled farmers along the Nile had to solve problems similar to those that faced the first farmers in Mesopotamia. The solutions were similar—building dikes, digging channels, and creating artificial lakes and pools.

These early projects in flood control and land drainage were carried on by cooperative efforts among members of the tribes that were living in the region. By about 4000 B.C.E., such works were well under way. These early Egyptians learned how to add to their arable land by draining previously unusable swamp areas.

Though these basic technical skills increased, full-fledged civilization had not yet appeared. Graves by the thousands survive from this period. Yet none is outstandingly large or elaborate. No evidence appears of individual priority, wealth, or power to control. Egyptians lived in some thirty or forty regions, each tribal group having its own distinctive totem animal or mascot. In time, these totems developed into a vast number of deities—part animal, part human in form. There were districts identified with the cat, lion, ram, crocodile, hawk, and so on. These were survivals, into the age of the neolithic farming techniques, from the tribal totems of hunting ancestors.

Between 4000 and 3100 B.C.E. conditions changed rather rapidly. The small provinces populated by free and equal farmers were changed into petty states ruled by local lords or chiefs, whose positions became hereditary. Out of the many provinces finally emerged two great groupings: one of the Lower Kingdom in the northern Nile delta; and the other of the Upper Kingdom in the southern Nile valley.

Rulers of the Lower and Upper Kingdoms struggled for supremacy. Finally, an Upper Egyptian ruler called Menes, sometimes Narmer, was able to weld together the first united Egyptian kingdom. His capital was established at Memphis about 3200 B.C.E. Thus began the first of more than thirty dynasties or royal families of native Egyptian rulers who held, or sought to hold, the throne of Egypt during nearly 3000 years following.

Now appears the state of affairs called civilization. Wealth flowed increasingly to the great landowners and landlords, including the kings or pharaohs; the regional provincial rulers known as *nomarchs;* the generals and officers of the armies of the king and nobles; the priests, who became both numerous and powerful in Egypt; and a large class of managers, overseers, stewards, and scribes, who were needed to run the rich estates of rulers, nobles, and priests.

Slaves toiled also in this civilized Egypt. They served mainly in the residences, shops, and storehouses of the rich and of royalty. Labor on the land was performed by peasants who were, in effect, serfs. They belonged to the land they worked. Their master was the owner of the land; if the land was given away or taken, they went with it.

Egyptian civilization rested now on a foundation similar in important respects to what later was called feudalism. Basically, despite manifest differences in language, religion, art, and customs, the civilizations of Egypt and Mesopotamia had much in common with the social structure of feudal Europe.

## EARLY PERIODS AND INFLUENCES
## IN EGYPTIAN HISTORY

Early Egyptian history remains unclear. Even dates for known rulers and dynasties are uncertain: Egyptologists agree in outlining the principal stages of that history. They group the thirty-one known dynasties into nine major periods. The first two dynasties form the initial or "Early Dynastic Period" which lasted some 400 years, from about 3100 to 2686 B.C.E. Next, including the Third through Sixth dynasties, came the "Old Kingdom Period," about 500 years long from 2686 to 2181 B.C.E.

The most famous pyramids of ancient Egypt were built during that Old Kingdom Period. The influences and forerunners of those pyramids, however, can be traced back to the Early Dynastic Period.

Again we find east-to-west influences at work. Some students see in Egyptian hieroglyphs a derivation from the Sumerian hieroglyphic writing. Also there is evidence in the seals. Seals, bearing identifying symbols in relief, were first developed in Mesopotamia. They were used to imprint records on moist clay. Sometimes the seals were flat disks, sometimes rollers bearing indentations. Such seals have been found with pictures of Mesopotamian buildings that show a distinctive style of indented panels formed in their brick walls. Egyptian tombs from the Early Dynastic Period show similar exterior designs. These likenesses seem too striking to be merely a matter of chance.

In materials, too, these Egyptian tombs resembled the Mesopotamian buildings shown on the seals. They were all made of mud bricks. However, the purposes of the structures were quite different. Those in Mesopotamia were intended to house the living, as temples, places of worship, or palaces. The comparable Egyptian structures were, however, tombs for the dead.

## DEDICATED TO DEATH

No other civilization ever devoted so much attention, labor, and wealth to the effort to preserve, shelter, and tend the remains of its dead men and rich rulers. During the three thousand years of

Egypt's greatness, the enduring structures built were not mansions for the rich, palaces for rulers, or even fortifications for cities. They were, almost without exception, private tombs.

A man's status could be estimated most accurately by the kind of tomb prepared during his life to receive his preserved corpse, or mummy, after death. The masses of peasants, serfs, slaves, and poor craftsmen simply disappeared after death, so far as survival of their bodies was concerned. Only the great were sealed away in extraordinary structures designed to outlast the ages—to mock at time.

Why such extraordinary stress on shelter and furnishings for the dead? The pyramids themselves put this question to us insistently today.

## UNDERSTANDING HOW MEN THOUGHT
## IN TIMES PAST

Some scholars have concluded that the past is really beyond recapture. They admit that we can still list dates, establish external events, and compile facts, but they deny that we can hope to understand the attitudes and beliefs of people in the distant past. Perhaps the most pungent statement of this belief that the past is sealed off from us is found in the philosophical drama, *Faust,* by Goethe (1749–1832), the famous German poet. In a scene, an eager but unimaginative student named Wagner speaks of his joy at the prospect of being able to enter into the spirit of past times. Doctor Faust, his teacher, warns him:

> My friend, the ages of the past
> Are books by seven seals protected.
> And what to you seems spirit of past times
> Is nothing but the spirit of men's minds
> In which those times have been reflected.
> And what we find distorted there
> Is truly oftentimes a sad affair!

> *—Translated for this book by H.A.K.*

In other words, history really reveals to us only the attitudes of the historians who have written it, not of the people about whom they wrote.

Others, however, take a more hopeful view of the quest. One such was Thomas Browne, a physician, antiquarian, and man-of-letters of seventeenth century England. He was fascinated by relics of the past, especially those having to do with tombs and disposal of the dead. In a strange work called *Urn Burial,* Browne wrote:

> "What song the Sirens sang, or what name Achilles assumed when he hid himself among women, though puzzling questions, are not beyond all conjecture."

The stories of the Sirens and of Achilles came from Homer's epic, *The Iliad* and *The Odyssey.* Browne regarded them as historical sources as well as literature. The tantalizing gaps in these histories he was willing, perhaps even eager, to fill in by means of conjecture.

In what follows we may be closer to the method of Dr. Browne than to the warning of Dr. Faust. We seek to make the pyramids more than mere masses of stone left to puzzle later ages.


## FROM THE HERE TO THE HEREAFTER
## IN ANCIENT EGYPT

Egyptians from their earliest days believed that a man's fortunes in the afterlife depended largely on how his corpse was cared for on earth. His soul or spirit or surviving vital spark could continue and prosper only if his remains were properly preserved and protected.

In a curiously material and matter-of-fact way, they believed that bodily needs continued after death. The surviving spirit needed suitable food, drink, and other material comforts. If these were not provided in some usable form, then the afterlife could be miserable or even end in annihilation.

It is not always clear to us just where the Egyptians believed that a good afterlife would be enjoyed. Commonly, they pictured the afterlife as a pleasant underworld, lying below the western horizon. There, each evening, the sun went down, obeying the rule of the great sun-god *Re* (or Ra). They called their blessed region "the Fields of Reeds," as the Greeks later called theirs "the Elysian Fields."

If the corpse had been properly preserved and the tomb had the right design, then the spirit should be able to make its way via the pit of the tomb itself to those blessed fields of reeds. Tomb design and furnishings were thus of truly vital importance.

People of power and wealth planned and paid for their tombs to be prepared while they were still very much alive. A tomb was no mere temporary shelter for remains that would return soon enough to the dust. Instead it was to be an eternal "house," intended to endure through an afterlife that might be endless.

Such a house clearly called for more careful and lasting construction than the houses they inhabited during the all-too-few years of their lives before death.

Egyptian ideas and customs concerning death did not remain rigidly fixed during all the thousands of years of their civilizations. New tendencies entered as ruling dynasties changed, and as outside influences interacted with their own traditions. Egyptian history had periods of unified rule and stability, punctuated by epochs of upheaval and civil strife. The numerous, powerful communities of priests also influenced traditional practices, usually to assure themselves greater influence and more status.

In the midst of such changes, attention remained focused on the design and preparation of the tomb itself. And if successful scribes or powerful landowners lavished wealth on their tombs, how much more elaborate must be the tomb prepared for a king of united Egypt! According to the state religion these rulers were no mere mortals; they were divine beings, expressly created to rule over the great land.

After death, a king's divinity was realized. Then, at last, his spirit-body could rejoin and unite with the powerful god who had created him. It could do that, however, only if his body had been properly prepared and entombed.

Egypt had accumulated hundreds, even thousands, of tribal, local, and regional gods. The sun-god *Re*, however, was the supreme national deity during the period in which the pyramids came into being.

Egyptian rulers had added reason to desire obviously permanent and protected tombs. This would assure all who saw those tombs that the king whose mummy was secreted within had surely been merged with his maker, the mighty *Re*, and was even now helping send the rays of the sun down to bless and make fruitful the Egyptian lands.

There are suggestions of this belief in the fascinating Egyptian story of Sinuhe. The pharaoh Amenemhet I had just died. The story relates that Amenemhet flew off to the blessed regions and there was united with the Sun "and the god's body was merged with his creator." The "god's body" means the spirit-body of the dead king. The "creator" was *Re*. Henceforth, each morning the transfigured king would rise and shine with the sun, and each evening descend to the blessed fields of reeds.

Such ideas made a ruler's tomb and burial procedures the most important single concern in his life.

## EARLY BURIAL PRACTICES

Egyptian tombs and entombments became increasingly elaborate through passing centuries. The earliest surviving tombs were simple, but they came in the early stages of civilization and before the dynasties of divine kings. These earliest tombs were dug in the dry sand, beyond reach of the Nile floods. The body, wound in a reed mat as a shroud, was laid here, with some lifetime possessions— ornaments, hunting gear, and also food and drink in containers.

The bodies in this dry sand quickly dessicated and became mummylike. However, in time the covering sand would shift or be blown away. The bodies, then exposed, soon fell to bits and disappeared. Seeing this, the living feared the same would some day be the fate of their own corpses.

During the First Dynastic Period, kings and nobles began to prepare their tombs with oblong covers formed from mud bricks. When the sand drifted over these tomb tops, they looked something like the outdoor benches on which Egyptians later liked to sit and gossip. Thus in after-years the Arabic word *mastaba,* or "bench," became the name for these pre-pyramid tombs.

A typical mastaba included a series of shallow chambers, partly below ground, partly above. A central pit received the corpse in its box or coffin. Chambers on either side contained the personal possessions left with the dead man.

Many separate rectangular cells formed small "rooms" in the roof structure. These held containers of food and drink, tools and utensils, and so on. Mastabas became many-chambered apartments, to assure the fulfillment of all the material wants of the dead occupant.

They might contain even a small boat, models of buildings, and sometimes the bodies of servants who had waited on the occupant of the main tomb. I. E. S. Edwards, a leading authority on the pyramids, points out that these servants most likely had administered poison to themselves as "a duty required by their terms of employment" after their master's death. Thus social and class distinctions were perpetuated into the afterlife.

During the Second and Third dynasties, mastaba tombs began to be built with larger and more complex superstructures above the burial pits. By the Fourth Dynasty some tombs were being constructed of stone rather than of mud bricks.

Multiple chambers and halls appear in such constructions dating from the Fifth and Sixth dynasties. Their walls show pictures of the lifetime activities of the occupant of the tomb. He is depicted hunting, inspecting his estates, conducting business transactions. The estate activities are also shown: harvest and processing of foods, handcrafting of various goods, and the serving of food and drink to the master.

We can be sure that such pictures were not intended to comfort the bereaved mourners. The interior was sealed against entry, once the corpse had been laid inside. These pictures were there because of the belief that they could assure the dead man the same activities and pleasures in the afterlife.

Somehow a picture was believed to be an effective substitute for what it represented. For instance, pictures or images of food and drink were included to nourish the spirit-body, if real food should become exhausted in the tomb.

Likewise, substitution was applied even to the dead body. Clearly the corpse might decompose in the tomb even though mummified, or perhaps might be destroyed by tomb plunderers. Hence a statue or even a picture of the dead occupant was commonly placed near his mummy. To make sure that the spirit would recognize this body image as its own, the name, titles, and other facts about the dead man were included in writing. The afterlife thus included not only eating, drinking, being waited on, managing spirit-estates—but even reading!

Other mortuary inscriptions might identify persons in group scenes placed on the wall of the tomb. I. E. S. Edwards says that these were usually relatives or servants of the dead man, "who were thus assured of an afterlife in the service of their master."[3]

Mastaba tombs of the great were also provided with frequent food deliveries. They were placed on a special altar outside a false door in the superstructure of the tomb. Such a "picture of a door" was suited for use by the hungry spirit when it felt the need to feed.

The first such catering services to the corpse were placed there by a surviving son or family member. Later, priests contracted to continue such servings, year after year. Lavish gifts were made to pay such "mortuary priests" for these attentions.

In the time of the pyramids, a son of the Pharaoh Khafra (Chephren), gave to such priests a dozen towns complete with their lands and inhabitants. In return the priests were pledged to provide food and drink for the tomb. Finally, the tombs were inscribed with traditional magic spells and formulas. If all other sources of food, drink, and services were to fail, these might satisfy the needs of the insatiable spirit.

Thus the tombs of Egypt's great became ever more elaborate and lasting homes for spirit-beings who insisted somehow on living much as they had lived while still on earth.


IMHOTEP'S INNOVATION

The mastaba tombs, while growing larger and more complex, still remained basically oblong. They did not resemble pyramids. That form appears almost suddenly in the tomb of a King Zoser (or Djoser) early in the Third Dynasty, between 2690 and 2680 B.C.E., which opened the Old Kingdom Period of history.

The real hero of this pyramid innovation was Zoser's architect, engineer, and physician, Imhotep, an all-around genius, almost of

the caliber of Leonardo da Vinci. Imhotep designed a stepwise or staggered shape, not a smooth pyramid. Though severely damaged, it still stands at Saqqara, overlooking the site of Memphis.

From a great base, 411 by 358 feet, rose its six unequal steps, or stages, to a top more than 200 feet high. Seen from the sides, its edges showed a zigzag or stepwise profile. Apparently the summit itself did not end in a point, but rather in a small square platform.

Its exterior was surfaced with dressed limestone. There is evidence that this first pyramid was started as a mastaba tomb, but that the design was altered while construction was already under way.

Below the Step Pyramid, as Zoser's monument was called, a deep shaft leads down to a network of halls and chambers cut into the rock and elaborately decorated. The entire structure was surrounded at ground level by a large enclosure. It contained, among other buildings, a magnificent mortuary temple, with walls paneled in limestone and columns carved in lotus designs.

It was a sudden and stupendous triumph of ingenuity and art. This appears to have been recognized at once, for later kings of the Third Dynasty continued to build tombs in the step-pyramid style introduced by Imhotep. At least five other step pyramids are known to have been started and carried to varying degrees of completion. Zoser's, however, remains the best preserved as well as the most significant of them all.

## THE PERFECT PYRAMID APPEARS

The next great innovation came at the start of the Fourth Dynasty. It was the true or perfect pyramid form, free from steps. This is the familiar shape with square base, its four sides sloping equally and evenly to meet at the apex on top.

The first such pyramid is located about 30 miles south of the Memphis site, at Meidum, where it was completed about 2600 B.C.E. What one sees there now looks more like the remains of a tall tower with tapering sides than a pyramid, for it has been severely damaged. Under the sand at the base, however, remain portions of the complete pyramid as they appeared some 4500 years ago. The present "tower" is part of the inner core of the former pyramid. Its base measured 470 feet on a side, indicating how size had grown since the first Step Pyramid of Zoser.

This first true pyramid did not stand alone. It was surrounded by several related structures, parts of the typical pattern of a pyramid establishment. They included: (1) a mortuary or funeral temple, designed for services for the dead, and (2) a graded causeway or road, which led to (3) a valley building, which in turn was connected by (4) a canal to the nearby river Nile; and (5) a secondary or associated pyramid.

All the major pyramids built from this time on included similar groups of interrelated structures. The second, third, and fourth (above) were used to bring the royal corpse to its final resting place. Then the temple was at hand for the unending services of food, offerings, prayers, and physical protection. Other functions of these associated structures can be surmised today but not proved.

The first true pyramid at Meidum may have been prepared for Seneferu, first of the Fourth Dynasty kings of Egypt. If not, then it was surely started not long before his reign began. We know, at any rate, that by the time Seneferu died and was mummified, the pure or geometrical pyramid had become the accepted burial place for an Egyptian monarch.

It was Seneferu's son and successor, Khufu, or Cheops—as the Greeks called him—who became the greatest pyramid builder of all time. Today when most people speak of "the pyramids of Egypt," they have in mind the famous group of three near Giza. And of this trio, the Great Pyramid of Khufu overshadows the other two.

## THE PYRAMID GROUP AT GIZA

Here are the measurements of the three Giza pyramids, all erected during the Fourth Dynasty, the peak period for such tomb construction:

(1) Khufu's Great Pyramid—756 feet on a side, with base area of more than 571,000 square feet, or about thirteen acres.

(2) Khafra's Pyramid—708 feet on a side, base area more than 501,000 square feet.

(3) Menkaura's Pyramid, also called the Pyramid of Mycerinus —356 feet on a side, base area slightly below 128,000 square feet.

The Khafra pyramid's total bulk is about eight times that of the Menkaura tomb. Khufu's pyramid is, however, between nine and one-half and ten times the bulk of Menkaura's. Thus Khufu's giant exceeds the combined volumes of its two companions at Giza, large as they are.

These three neighboring tombs are the oldest complete stone structures in the world. Though their pyramidal shapes are clear, they are far from intact. They have been robbed of almost all the outer limestone jackets that once made their sloping sides smooth.

We can reconstruct the magnificent titles that each of them was given. The smallest was named "Menkaura is divine." The next was "Khafra is great." The largest of all had a still larger title: it could be translated as "Khufu is one who belongs to the horizon."

## THE GREATEST OF PYRAMIDS

The apex of Khufu's huge tomb stood 481 feet above its base. Today the top is more than 30 feet lower, for the dozen topmost layers of stone have long been lost. Like the jacket of smooth *tufa,* limestone that once covered the sides, these stones have been taken largely for use in other buildings in the region.

Despite its staggering solid bulk, it was built with astounding accuracy. Though the sides of the base average 756 feet long, the difference between the longest and the shortest of them is a tiny fraction of one per cent.

About 2,300,000 separate stone blocks were prepared and assembled to form it. The average block weight is about two and one-half tons. Some single blocks weigh up to 15 tons.

Its proportions repeat ratios found in earlier pyramids. Thus its height of 481 feet was in the ratio of 7 to 11 to its base side of 756 feet. This is the same ratio found in the ruined Meidum tomb, the first true pyramid built.

Khufu's record pyramid was no mere enlargement of what had

gone before. It was planned as a complete and unique unit, outside and in. Intricate systems of internal chambers and passageways were part of its design. In the place of honor, midway between apex and base, is the royal chamber. Perhaps Khufu's mummy was stolen from it ages ago. No trace of that corpse remains on record.

The full scope and significance of the passageways and chambers is still being studied by specialists. The total mass of this stonework is almost too much to grasp. It includes stone weighing nearly six and one-half million tons. The combined bulk is nearly two and one-half times that of the entire Empire State Building, the tallest skyscraper yet built. The millions of pieces of cut limestone and granite were laid in about 200 courses or levels, each about two feet six inches thick.

Cutting and fitting were accomplished with extreme accuracy. Adjoining stones were so perfectly lined up that, it is said, not even a knifeblade could be slipped between them. Yet the builders had neither steel nor iron tools. They worked with copper chisels and saws. Also drills tipped with jewels were used by the quarrymen who first extracted the giant blocks and by the stonemasons who finally shaped them at the pyramid site itself.

To an extent we moderns can hardly imagine, this great stone mountain at Giza was literally "made by hand." Human muscle, sweat, and skill accomplished the entire task from start to finish. First, the giant stones were cut in distant quarries, then dragged to the Nile bank, then floated on great barges to landing wharfs, then dragged up an enormous ramp whose slope was increased as the pyramid rose higher. The stupendous amount of human drudgery and skill seems today even more amazing than the physical measurements of the structure itself.

A TRAVELER'S TALE OF THE GREAT PYRAMID

About 450 B.C.E. that eager, inquisitive, and gossipy Greek, Herodotus, visited the Giza pyramids. Like most who came to gaze, he had no notion of the true age of these stone mountains. They were by that time some 2000 years old!

Herodotus told the world how the Great Pyramid had been built.

His information came from the surviving Egyptian priests, spokes-men for an ancient religion which by 450 B.C.E. had decayed and become distorted in an age of prevailing Greek influences. Accordingly, his report has to be taken as hearsay, and carefully weighed against known facts.

He wrote that the Great Pyramid had required twenty years to build. This is possible, for Khufu seems to have been on the throne about twenty-three years in all. Herodotus said that during all those twenty years an army of 100,000 men had been constantly kept at work, but in rotation, with a fresh crew replacing the previous one every three months. This is now believed to be an over-estimate. Recent commentators believe that the labor force reached 100,000 only between July and late October when farm work was impos-sible due to the annual Nile floods. During the rest of the year these human beasts of burden would return to their tasks as serfs on the land.

Meanwhile, from September to July, a permanent nucleus of expert craftsmen continued at the quarries, cutting stone blocks from the solid rock. Another large group of expert stonemasons worked on at the pyramid site, shaping and trimming the blocks already there, so they would be ready to be placed in the rising structure. These two permanent work crews together may have aver-aged about ten thousand members.

Thus the heavy work of stone transport would be concentrated into the flood months, when the labor force might reach 100,000. However, the total human labor—if this theory is correct—was prob-ably not over forty to fifty percent of the amount that Herodotus reports. His figures work out to two million man-years. Even the reduced amount of 800,000 to one million man-years is a gigantic outlay of human toil, however!

The social effects were certainly far-reaching. Herodotus stated that "ten years' oppression of the people" had been required just to construct the 3000-foot causeway over which the blocks were dragged from the quarries to the barges that carried them along the Nile to the landings where they were taken ashore near the pyramid site.

Also, Herodotus heard from the priests that the ancient tyrant,

Khufu, had closed temples and forbidden religious offerings, presumably to force all possible resources and labor into the building of his tomb. Thus Khufu had acquired a bad name with the priests, and this too had become part of the continuing tradition of the great pyramids.

When we turn from the hearsay and traditions reported by Herodotus to the more objective findings of Egyptian archaeology, or Egyptology as it is often called, we find striking indications that Khufu's enormous project had to be the last of its scope. The Old Kingdom Period, that heyday of pyramid building, lasted about 500 years. During this time a major pyramid was begun, on the average, about once every twenty-two or twenty-three years. Yet the actual volume of such construction was not evenly spread out. If we compare the bulks, in cubic feet or cubic yards, of known pyramids, we find there must have been more such building during the 200 years after the appearance of the original Step Pyramid of Zoser, than there was in all the 700 years which followed those two centuries.

Those 700 years came to an end, about 1775 B.C.E., with the building of the last known true pyramid of Egypt. It belonged to Khjender, a king of the Eighteenth Dynasty. It was a mere shrunken mound, with a base only 170 feet on a side. Its bulk was barely three percent that of Khufu's enormous tomb!

What forces were at work even in the closing years of the Old Kingdom Period to reverse the trend toward ever more enormous pyramid tombs? During the earliest royal dynasties of Egypt, the rulers of the nomes, or districts, had been appointed by the king in Memphis. When such nomarchs died, or displeased the king, they were replaced at his pleasure. However, by the Fifth and Six Dynasties the positions of the nomarchs had become hereditary. They thus became minor monarchs, or princes, who regarded their territories as their own property rather than that of the king in Memphis.

Also, as the desire for larger and more elaborate pyramid tombs had grown, the kings of Egypt began to make gifts of such tombs to favorite officers and courtiers. A pyramid, by itself, was insufficient. It had to be serviced by priests who provided the food, drink, and rituals for the tomb's occupant. Hence, the kings would give their favorites also valuable lands or estates whose produce was to be used to pay the priests to provide such continuing attentions to the dead. Or the land might be given directly to the groups and associations of priests. In any case, with the land went the peasants who labored on it. Such gift estates were usually excused from paying taxes or contributing shares of their crops to the storehouses of the king.

The result was during the latter part of the Old Kingdom Period, the kings of Egypt, though still reputed to be divine, grew actually less wealthy and less powerful. More income and influence accumulated in the hands of their subordinate princes or nomarchs and among the priestly groups—whose members were usually chosen from the sons of these same ruling families.

These great landowning aristocrats wanted all the labor of the peasants on their estates. They opposed any such mass labor draft as that which built the pyramid of Khufu during so many years. The lessened labor and wealth at the disposal of the kings were reflected in smaller pyramids built to receive their mummies.


REVOLT AND CONFUSION

Finally, about 2200 B.C.E. outright rebellion flared. The land of Egypt was no longer united: it was split into separate, warring districts, ruled by their nomarchs and was sunk in outright civil war. This was the so-called "First Intermediate Period," lasting about fifty years (about 2181–2133). Only one pyramid is known to have been started during this era.

During this interval of conflict and change, tombs and temples dating from the preceding Old Kingdom Period were often looted and damaged. Perhaps hungry peasants seized opportunities to strike back for all the years of sweating labor that had raised such luxurious homes for dead kings and princes.

Chronicles dealing with this period, according to N. M. Nickolsky, the Russian historian, report that the peasants "laid hand to weapons and all the land was stricken with rebellion." It was told further that some peasants who belonged to estates held by temples, like the Temple of the god *Re* in Om, took the land for their own use. They seized offerings from the storehouses belonging to the priests, and "fed on the sacrificial bread." Some peasants, it was told, even moved into the so-called towns of the dead and dared to occupy the residences of the mortuary priests who had tended the tombs of the great.

Finally, a nomarch or prince from Upper Egypt forced his way to the top, defeating all rivals, and established his family as a new dynasty over Egypt. The capital now was moved from Memphis to Thebes.

This marks the start of the Middle Kingdom Period, dating from about 2135 to 1785 B.C.E. It included the Eleventh and Twelfth Dynasties of Egypt. Its rulers built about eleven major pyramids of which traces remain today. None of these compared in size with the tomb of Khufu or of other huge pyramids of the Fourth Dynasty.

The concluding significant fact is that so far as can be determined today no major pyramid was begun after about 1775 B.C.E. If we take the date of the first true or geometrical pyramid, that at Meidum, as 2600 B.C.E., we find that slightly more than 800 years later pyramid building had come to an end. Eight centuries, against the vast scales of Egyptian civilization, are amazingly short in duration. During those eight centuries thirty to forty substantial pyramids, recognizable portions of which remain today, were started. (Estimates of the known pyramid relics in Egypt run as high as sixty or seventy. These estimates, however, include many fragments from which it is not possible to ascertain that they were ever completed or put into use.)

The greatest among the pyramids, however, proved incomparably enduring. Regarding those in the group at Giza, and some others at sites such as Saqqara, Dahshur, and Abu Sir, we can apply an old Arabic proverb inspired by these man-made mountains of stone erected in the hope of insuring immortality:

"Time mocks at all things, but the pyramids mock at time. . . ."

# V

## THE PARTHENON ON THE ACROPOLIS

---

## GREEK GLORY ON A HILLTOP

Earth proudly wears the Parthenon
As the best gem upon her zone.

— RALPH WALDO EMERSON, *The Problem*

The structure most widely admired for its beauty still stands, battered and incomplete but supremely lovely. The Parthenon on the Acropolis, once the citadel and sacred hill of the Athenian city-state during its brief golden age in the fifth century B.C.E., is still today the lofty landmark of the active, growing, modern Athens.

The Parthenon is a noble and an unforgettable ruin—damaged by warfare, violence, neglect, and worse during 2400 years. It was in 438 B.C.E. that the newly built Parthenon first kindled pride or provoked complaint from the lively, chattering, and inquisitive citizens of Athens. Excitement and elation were in the air. Improbable events occurring in swift succession, had put the Athens city-state in the forefront of Greek power and progress. The Parthenon was conceived as a marble and gold paean of victory, a perfect tribute to the great maiden goddess Athena, the deity to whom the city itself was dedicated.

Pericles, the unusual political leader of this even more unusual democracy, had pushed through the project. At its head were the finest artists of architecture and sculpture, as well as the most able artisans of an age when design and craftsmanship in stonework attained heights never previously approached.

The great Phidias, foremost painter and sculptor, executed the giant statue of Athena herself. It stood forty feet high within the Parthenon, a vision of rich ivory and heavy, gleaming gold overlaying the inner core of wood. It was visible through the open portals to sailors approaching on the Aegean Sea.

Phidias' pupils and associates had enriched the building with a wealth of statues and friezes blending so harmoniously with its form

75

that they and the Parthenon must have seemed inseparable—though now they are no longer united.

As for the building itself, its architects Ictinus and Callicrates seemed to have brought life to the fine marble quarried on Mount Pentilius and shaped into its lovely columns and pediments. Even the roofless ruin we see today radiates grace.

Stone had never before been shaped to such singing splendor. Here was a harmony both subtle and satisfying. No wonder that thousands of years after the Parthenon first stood proudly completed on the Acropolis, men would still measure each dimension and proportion, study its lines and subtle curves, pursuing secrets of a seeming perfection.

## HIGH ON A PEAK OF HISTORY

The imagination, ingenuity, and material means that produced the superb Parthenon and its approaches on the Acropolis, did not develop by accident. They flowed from events of a surprising six-year period, 485 to 479 B.C.E. Under the leadership of Athens, the city-states of Greece in that period defeated the powerful Persians, driving them from Europe, then followed up this victory by expanding their shipping, commerce, and control far beyond the Aegean Sea.

The first great Greek victory had come almost suddenly. In the summer of 480 B.C.E., the warriors of the Persian King Xerxes swarmed through Attica and into Athens, its principal city, looting and destroying. When the Persians departed, temples lay in ruins on the Acropolis, which served Athens as a site for ceremonial worship and for fortifications.

Then, only a few months later, the great naval battle of Salamis was fought. It swung the balance sharply in the other direction, for the resourceful Greek sea captains and sailors soundly drubbed the Persians. Before the end of 479 B.C.E., Greek victory in the Persian wars was assured, though "mopping up" operations by the Greeks continued for years in campaigns to free Greek cities of the Aegean from the last traces of Persian control.

Athenian leaders skillfully directed the policies of the association of Greek city-states so that it served their interests, and a growing flood of profits from shipping, trade, and tribute flowed toward the treasuries of Athens.

Pre-eminent among the democratically elected leaders in Athens was Pericles, a statesman of rare vision, resourcefulness, and eloquence. His public career began about 463 B.C.E. and continued for more than thirty years. He soon became the leader of the Athenian *demos,* or free citizens' party (hence our word "democratic").

The opposition was the party of the wealthy, the landowners, merchants, and their spokesmen. During the Periclean "golden age," democracy expanded. More and more social groups began to take part and vote in the councils and operations of their government. With their support, Pericles put through many great proposals for public works and for spreading more widely the new wealth that was now flowing to Greek cities in general, and to Athens especially.

## PLANS FOR THE ACROPOLIS

The temples on the Acropolis lay in ruins, as they had been left by the Persian invaders. The first impulse of the Athenians when they came home after their victory at Salamis was to leave these ruins—as a reminder. Now Pericles patiently and skillfully pushed through his plan—to build a great new temple there to Athena, where her image should stand enshrined in glory as a symbol of Athenian faith and fortune.

In 447 B.C.E., work began on the Parthenon, the greatest of the several structures destined to glorify the Acropolis. The building was finished about nine years later. The money that paid for it came from many sources. Now that the Persian treaty had been signed, there were tribute funds flowing in. There were taxes on shipping, harbor charges, transport, imports and exports, sales taxes, license fees, fines, and head taxes on slaves and on people set free from slavery.

The greatest monument of Greece's greatest age, the golden age, was paid for by a flow of gold and silver coins that seems large even now, especially when we compare it with the population of Athens and its surrounding area called Attica. Not more than a third of a million people lived there; quite possibly the figure was nearer a quarter of a million.

Between one-third and one-half of this population were slaves and aliens, deprived of the vote and not permitted to hold government positions. Nor were women, children, or young people under twenty-one included among the voting citizens. The assemblies of voters took place frequently in Athens, and many citizens who lived in outlying farm areas could not attend. Hence, the actual number of citizens who voted during this age of Athenian democracy could hardly have been more than 50,000, and may have been closer to 40,000.

Slavery was basic in this society. The slaves performed personal services for the wealthy. They also did menial tasks in what we might call "industry." They labored in the state-owned metal mines. They did the rough and dangerous work in shipyards, harbors, and warehouses. Slaves were bought and sold. The wealthy set up more and more mass workshops or manufacturing establishments. There slaves worked in groups, making various goods for sale.

Yet, during this brief golden or pinnacle period of Greek culture and art, new opportunities and influence were opening also for free sailors, workers, small merchants, and others. For them it was a period of expansion, optimism, and increasing awareness of their own interests and confidence in their ability to attain these interests. This was an age of active, talkative, inquisitive, gossiping, prying, critical, questioning, and oftentimes resentful and unreasonable activity by citizens. These were everyday men, very much part of the world around them, and for the most part far too occupied and interested to have time to wonder whether or not they were happy.

They would have been surprised, very likely, had they been told that they lived in a golden age. There were too many things each one wanted to see changed, but they might have agreed on one thing—that a free citizen of Athens should never have cause to envy the resident of any city anywhere else. They had no tyrant over them. They elected their officials—and could reject them, too.

From 447 to 438 B.C.E., artists, architects, stonemasons, mechanics, and slaves by the thousands were laboring to realize the plans for the Parthenon. Accounts kept in those days have been translated. They show that free citizens, aliens living in Athens, and slaves were employed on it, and that they all received "equal pay for equal work" regardless of their status in Athenian society.

The general level of prosperity was lifted by these continuing payments to workers and artists on the Parthenon and other public works during the era of Pericles. These projects served to distribute more broadly the income of tributes from military victories and profits from successful shipping and trading ventures. Pericles also arranged that Athenian citizens should be paid for jury duty and for attending the great traditional theatrical performances.

More people had reason to feel that the government of Athens was serving their interests as well as the interests of the wealthy landowners and merchants. The good things of life were being shared more widely during this golden age that centered around Athens for less than half a century. This greater sharing applied not only to what the Athenian citizens received *from* their city-state. It applied also to what they contributed *to* it. To a notable extent, they shared in decision-making and in the carrying out of decisions.

Pericles liked to say that under him Athens had grown to be "the school of Greece." Indeed, the greatest artists, poets, and philosopher-scientists of the era had been drawn to this remarkable little city, where they found appreciation and support.

THE PARTHENON AS SYMBOL OF A GREAT ERA

The Parthenon's marble remains on the Acropolis of Athens still remind the modern world of that Athens which somehow, almost suddenly and certainly briefly, reached historic greatness. The Parthenon today stands serene in majesty and simple beauty. The damage it has suffered adds to, rather than detracts from, its nobility.

Today, it bears no colors and it is only weathered marble. Depending on the light that falls on it from the sun and sky, that marble may show tones of off-white, ivory, amber, or even russet. Simplicity prevails and a noble harmony is revealed in the rows of great but graceful supporting columns, eight at front and back, and fifteen additional columns along each side. It is revealed also in the lovely proportion and slope of the pediments above the columns at either end, and in other proportions of the structure. The Parthenon as it now stands appears beyond any need for added ornament or decorative detail, for its form alone is so beautiful.

It may come as a surprise to learn how different was the completed Parthenon that became the pride of Athenian citizens in the late fifth century B.C.E. Rich and wonderful sculptures were worked into its structure. Bright colors were heavily applied to add contrast and emphasis. That original Parthenon was richly conceived, being abundantly decorated with carved figures of gods and men and forms of plants and flowers.

What we admire today is really only the over-all form that has survived. All but a few of the magnificent sculptures are gone. Some were totally and tragically destroyed. Others were removed and carried to Britain, where as "the Elgin Marbles" they are among the greatest treasures of the British Museum in London. Still others can be seen displayed in Greece.

Archaeologists and art historians have "rebuilt" this original Parthenon, by means of models and drawings. Little doubt remains as to its plan and how it looked. Nevertheless, we have to depend on guesswork or supposition for some of the most intriguing details, for they have totally disappeared.

Greek citizens of the golden age probably were most deeply impressed by the huge and costly gold-and-ivory statue of Athena carved by Phidias. It stood upright in the center of the building, in a *cella*, or chamber, divided into three sections or aisles by double rows of columns. A large part of Athens' gold reserves hung, like armor, in heavy sheets on the goddess. Athena, the maiden warrior among the Greek gods, was there for all to admire, a stupendous majesty, clad in helmet and armor, and armed with spear and shield. In one hand she held extended a small statuette of a female figure, symbolizing Victory. Nearby lay her sacred snake, resplendent and glittering.

Behind this dazzling and overpowering statue, a wall screened a smaller chamber which served as the temple treasury and was called the Room of the Virgins. Its Greek name, *parthenon*, became the name of the entire temple. The roof overhead was made of sheets of thin, translucent marble to admit light by day.

Though its central statue was heroic in size, the Parthenon is not a large building. Its outside length is about 230 feet, its width about 100 feet, and its height from base to top about 65 feet.

Its sculptures were varied. They were created by perhaps 100 different artists under the guidance of Phidias, and displayed in three-dimensional form many favorite events and heroes of Greek mythology. Also, they provided a magnificent panorama of Athenian people during a great festival.

The Parthenon faces east. In the flat angle formed by the gables of the roof over the great entrance gate were sculptures of several Olympian gods, including a group that represents the myth of the birth of Athena herself. She is said to have sprung fully grown from the forehead of her father, Zeus, king of the gods. The myth emphasized the association of Athena with reason and intellect. At the other end, facing west, the corresponding part of the Parthenon displayed sculptures of the struggle for the rule of Attica and Athens, in which Athena overcame Poseidon, god of the sea.

The architectural style of the Parthenon is Doric. The solid stone walls that enclosed the cella and parthenon chambers were set inward from the stately rows of columns that surround the outside. Between columns and walls is formed a sort of shallow surrounding porch or portico, extending completely around the building.

THE FAMOUS FRIEZE OF THE PARTHENON

Rather high up on the walls of these porticoes was placed a frieze. Its total length, around the four sides, was over 520 feet. It is perhaps the most famous of all relief sculptures. Today, the British Museum exhibits the originals of almost half of this frieze, as well as casts reproducing a considerable part of the remainder. The west frieze remains in Greece. The full frieze pictured typical groups of Athenians taking part in the climax of the great civic festival, the Panathenic, held every four years to honor Athena. The frieze depicts all kinds of Athenians in the procession of the *peplos*. The *peplos* was a great garment woven for the sacred statue of the goddess. It was so large that it was paraded through Athens and to the Acropolis displayed on the yard-arm of a full-sized sailing ship which was hauled along on rollers!

Here in stone, yet full of motion and reality, we see this great Panathenic Parade and its varied participants: horsemen, chariots, musicians; pedestrians, both men and women, youths and girls; bearers of wine and food; elders, counselors, and judges of the community; guards and marshalls of the parade; animals being led to sacrifice; and, finally, over the door that leads into the Parthenon itself, the frieze shows the *peplos,* folded after removal from the mast, being presented to Athena's priest and his helper.

This great stone record of Athenian life and ceremonies was only a little more than three feet high, and was mounted nearly forty feet above the floor of the portico. It sums up a world of observation and fine artistry. The very idea of democracy is pictorially represented in this unequaled frieze.

Other elaborate sculptures also were parts of the new Parthenon. Between the capitals on top of the columns and the roof itself is a fairly deep band of stone called the *entablature.* Usually this was divided into alternate decorative bands, called *triglyphs,* and panels, called *metopes.* More than ninety such panels, all around the Parthenon, carried deep-relief sculptures picturing incidents of sharp conflict from mythology. Here various sculptors had carved the struggles. Some showed battles between man-horse monsters, or Centaurs, and a Greek tribe called the Lapiths; others pictured events in the Trojan War as told in the Homeric epic; and still others revealed fights of Greeks against Amazons, and gods against giants.

Some of the *metope* sculptors had worked in styles that appear old-fashioned or archaic. The work of others was distinctly "modern"—that is, in the more free, flexible, breathing style now associated with the classic or golden age of Pericles. Here, again, we note how advanced the Parthenon must have seemed to many Athenians in the fifth century B.C.E.

## THE COLORFUL PARTHENON

Color was boldly used in this building. It was applied widely, with a determined hand. This new Parthenon was a vivid, even spectacular showplace for all Greeks to admire. "Color was used as a necessary element in the decoration . . . ," said G. Rodenwaldt. "All the ornamentation was colored . . ."[4] The decorative triglyphs were painted blue, while between them the metope panels were painted with red backgrounds, suggesting conflict or bloodshed, perhaps. Backgrounds of the great processional frieze were blue, also. Other areas were painted bright yellow.

Even the sculptured figures themselves were painted in vivid colors except where human skin was represented. For such parts, the natural whiteness of the marble was given a more fleshlike hue by means of a stain prepared from milk and saffron, a plant with a yellow-orange pigment.

Hundreds of small ornamental stone decorations, now vanished from the roofless ruin, appeared also on the original Parthenon. In spite of its exquisite harmony of shape and proportion, the over-all effect was far from severe and restrained. Rather, it must have conveyed a mood of exuberance, of self-assurance, and even of triumph. It was, after all, a sort of symphony in stone, giving thanks for the Athenian victories over the Persians—and over poverty.

## THE VIOLENT HISTORY OF THE PARTHENON

Between the end of the golden age of Greece and the present, the Parthenon went through a fantastic sequence of change and damage. Even a bare summary makes one wonder that what survives is complete enough to suggest its essential beauty and perfection.

Athens lost its one-time leadership and power among the Greek city-states. Greeks, as well as most of the known world, came under the domination of a new, aggressive, and brutal civilization centered in another famous city-state—Rome, Italy. In spite of the wear and tear of time, during about 600 years, the Parthenon and other ceremonial structures on the Acropolis were maintained for worship of the Olympian gods.

In the third or fourth century C.E. (Christian Era), new dangers of invasion led to the conversion of the Acropolis hill into a fortification with great gates and towers. The first real damage to the Parthenon dates from about that time.

Early in the fifth century, Theodosius II, Emperor of the Eastern or Byzantine Empire, ordered the old Olympian religion abolished, to clear the field for Christianity. This meant the end of all worship of Athena. The Parthenon was taken over and converted into a Christian church. Early Christian mosaics were placed inside, and many drastic alterations were made in the famous pagan temple.

Phidias' giant gold-and-ivory statue of Athena was removed and carried off to the capital of the empire, Constantinople, now called Istanbul. According to the report repeated by a number of recent historians, the statue reached Constantinople during the reign of the famous Emperor Justinian (483–565 C.E.) and was set up in the forum of that great city.

There the statue stood like a trophy of some war, not an object of worship, during more than six centuries. In the year 1204 the army of the Fourth Crusade, European Christians supposedly on their way to rescue the Holy Land from the Moslem infidels, paused to plunder the capital of the Christian Eastern Empire.

John Beckwith wrote about the battle: "In the course of the fighting a fire destroyed a large part of the city . . . and one night a drunken, hysterical mob hacked to pieces the great statue of Athena . . . because the goddess seemed to be beckoning to the invader."[5]

If this was the end of that great statue by Phidias, it was 1640 years old at the time of that destruction. No trace of it has ever been reported since that time, nor does there remain any drawing or sketch made while it still existed.

The Parthenon in the seventh century C.E. became a Christian church dedicated to Santa Sophia. Still later, the great structure originally built to honor the Virgin Athena was rededicated, this time to the Virgin Mary.

At the start of the thirteenth century, the Crusaders invaded Athens. The Parthenon and other churches (basilicas) which had been under the Orthodox religion now became for a time Roman Catholic. The bishop for the area had his residence on the Acropolis. Near the end of the fourteenth century, the Turks conquered the Acropolis but were later driven out by the forces of the Republic of Venice, who added to the fortifications.

By 1460, however, the Turks were back again in control. They converted the Parthenon into a Mohammedan mosque. A minaret was erected, piercing the roof and rising high above the building. Part of the Parthenon became the lodging of a Turkish official. A nearby building housed the harem of the Turkish commander.

The greatest single damage to the Parthenon dates from the Turkish-Venetian war in the late seventeenth century. In 1687 while the Parthenon was being used as a Turkish arsenal, a shot from a nearby hill penetrated its roof and set off the powder stored inside. Huge sections of the building were devastated.

The victory of the Venetians was celebrated in part by the shipping to Venice of various sculptures gathered on the Acropolis by the victorious commander, Francesco Morosini.

Turkish rule returned and a small mosque was built, this time within the ruins of the Parthenon itself. It occupied the very area where Phidias' great statue of Athena once had stood. Nearby was erected the customary minaret from which faithful Moslems were called for prayer.

## THE ELGIN MARBLES

During the eighteenth century, the damage to the remaining Parthenon sculptures continued more rapidly than ever. It was clear to the few who cared that they were doomed unless somehow they could be preserved. One who watched them with keen interest was Thomas Bruce, Lord Elgin, the British ambassador to the Turkish sultan in Constantinople.

He secured from the sultan permission to take "miscellaneous marbles" from the Parthenon. Removal and shipment to England involved difficulties, delays, and accidents. Finally, in 1814 the sculptures that had survived were exhibited in London. Artists and art-lovers were amazed and enthralled by them. A new realization of Greek artistic glory swept through the intellectual life of the day. Soon afterward, Lord Elgin, in need of funds, offered his marbles for sale to the British government. The matter was argued back and forth in Parliament. At last, the purchase was arranged for the equivalent of about $100,000. In 1816, these matchless sculptures from the greatest monument of the golden age of Greece were enshrined in the British Museum.

Greeks today call the action a theft by Lord Elgin, connived in by the sultan. Those who take the general British point of view insist that it was a great rescue of treasures that would otherwise have been destroyed or lost entirely.

## SECRETS OF THE PARTHENON REVEALED

Increasing appreciation and study were now turned toward the remains of the Parthenon itself. Its magic of form must surely be traceable to basic design. During the first half of the nineteenth century, a few devoted investigators began to make accurate measurements.

The findings revealed almost unbelievable subtlety and sophisticated knowledge on the part of the Greek architects of the Periclean period. The planners of the Parthenon appeared to have greater understanding of optical illusions and the effects of intersecting or parallel lines than the best architects of today.

It has been said, perhaps a little too broadly, that there were no strictly straight lines anywhere in the original Parthenon—only marvelous delicate curves that account for the total impression of lightness and grace. Every essential or critical line has been modified to produce the perfect effect in the eyes of the onlooker. We can only wonder how the Greeks gained so deep an understanding, or how their craftsmen were able to realize these intricate forms in stones, shaped by hand and joined without cement.

What are some of the "secrets" of shape in this subtlest of all great structures? The base or platform of stone on which it stands was made to billow upward slightly, in order that it should not look as if the rows of columns were ramming it down into the earth. The upper step, called the *stylobate*, has a tiny upward curve in the center when looked at from the front or back of the building. Its middle thus rises higher than its two ends by about one-thousandth of the distance between those two ends.

When looked at from the sides, the upper step also curves upward from its ends to its center by a similarly small proportion. The curves thus formed in stone are segments of circles whose center would be some three to four miles deep in the earth.

The exterior columns, forty-six in number, are five times as tall as they are wide. They appear to taper from bottom to top, but actually they are not formed in straight lines. Their shape is rather that of a cigar. The curvature, called *entasis*, gives them a maximum diameter nearly three-quarters of an inch greater than their base diameter. This maximum diameter is found about forty percent of the way from base to top. The result is a lightness and harmony unsurpassed by columns anywhere. Even the doors are not truly rectangular. They, too, were shaped with subtle *entasis*.

But there is more to the Parthenon's subtle magic of form; its columns do not point straight up in the air. They are not truly parallel, though they appear as such. The four corner columns are so slightly slanted inward that if their center lines could be continued upward, they would meet at a height of about one and one-half miles above the building. Every detail was given the same loving and knowing care. There is a multitude of tiny but effective deviations from uniformity, from truly right-angles, and from strict parallelism.

## PARTIAL RECONSTRUCTION OF THE PARTHENON

Aware at last that one of the world's greatest treasures of design and construction lay devastated on the Acropolis, the Greek government in the period of the late 1920s and early 1930s arranged for limited reconstruction and repair under expert supervision.

True restoration would be impossible for many reasons. A so-called "restoration," in which modern materials would be intermingled with the old would be a mistake, in the opinion of leading authorities. The present compromise, it has been said, has made the Parthenon as complete as it ever can be made—and more beautiful than it has been since the damage that occurred nearly 300 years ago.

The appeal of the ruined Parthenon is undeniable. Many travelers believe it to be the most memorable structure they have seen. Its impression varies with shifting patterns of sky and clouds by day. Night brings new and different magic with the light of the moon and of modern electric illumination. Its bold and commanding site, 200 feet above the streets of busy Athens, contributes to its power to catch and hold the attention.

Most of us feel greater understanding today for the ideas and attitudes of the golden age of Greece than for those of the pyramid-building monarchs of Egypt or the Mesopotamia of the days when Babylon was powerful and the ziggurats rose above the valley floor. Similarly, the language of form expressed by the Parthenon seems to us more familiar and less in need of interpretation than that of the ziggurats and the pyramids.

Though incomplete and stripped, this remnant of a master temple attracts the eye and kindles the imagination more than the original and perfect Parthenon might have done, had it been preserved intact through the ages.

# VI

## THE GREAT WALL OF CHINA

---

## THE GREATEST WALL OF ALL

. . . miles of fertile ground
With walls and towers were girdled round . . .

—COLERIDGE, *Kubla Khan,* or *A Vision in a Dream*

One of the most most far-reaching and stupendous of all great structures is a chain of barriers called *The Great Wall of China*. In many respects it is without a peer or a parallel and is likely to remain so in this modern world where walls and shields have lost their power to protect against nuclear warfare. The Great Wall network combined fortification, communication, and transportation functions. Its linked elements extended from the shores of the Pacific Ocean all the way east to the hilly country of Tibet. Its first segments, completed about 230 B.C.E., totaled between 1800 and 1900 miles in length. Later additions increased that total to more than twice as much, about 3900 miles.

Its full extent compares impressively with the dimensions of the great round earth itself. A trip around the world in an east or west direction crosses 360 meridians of longitude. The Great Wall crosses twenty-two such meridians—from 98° at its western end to 120° at its eastern, or Pacific end. Distances from the north pole to the south pole are marked off by 180 parallels of latitude. The Wall, in its course, wanders back and forth across six such parallels from the thirty-fifth to the forty-first parallels of the north hemisphere. The bulk of material that was piled into this huge obstacle against invaders would form a barrier six feet thick and ten feet tall all around the world at the equator. Beside this, vast quantities of stone, brick, and earth were used in repairing and rebuilding the Great Wall segments through the centuries.

A Portuguese traveler who visited China during the sixteenth century C.E., when the Great Wall was about 1800 years old, found 300,000 men at work to maintain it. How much human labor built the original Great Wall? A fair estimate seems to be at least twenty-five million man-years and maybe much more than that for the entire 3900 miles of wall. This is equal to the labor of a million men each working twenty-five years, or of five million men each working five years.

The wall traverses a wide variety of terrain. It winds over plains, mountains, valleys, deserts. It leads uphill and down, sometimes rising to altitudes between four and five thousand feet, and descending into desolate land below sea level. Defensive strength, not ease of construction, dictated the choice of locations when it was laid out.

The Great Wall was not intended to stand alone and unattended in its task of safeguarding the settled civilization to the south from the nomadic Mongol barbarians to the north. It was meant to contain and give power to a vigilant, trained defensive force—China's ever watchful armies of the Wall. These armies, at times, totaled a million men or more.

The Wall itself was built in sections linked by defense towers. They were placed between 300 and 800 feet apart, close enough so that their bowmen could shoot to hit attackers anywhere between. The number of such towers in the full length of the Wall is estimated at about 25,000. Each was tapered, being about forty feet square at bottom and about thirty feet square at its parapet forty feet above. Still another large group of towers stood entirely apart from the walls. There were perhaps an additional 15,000 of these free-standing lookout towers, heavily protected and provisioned, placed on sites where they commanded views of strategic areas of the nomad country. Such separate towers have been called the "early warning system" for the Great Wall itself. By fire or other signals, the lookouts could alert the force in the main Wall, if they spotted anything suspicious.

Thus, in its planning, construction, operation, and maintenance the Great Wall involved vast masses of human beings. By the millions they patrolled, stood watch, reconnoitered, drilled, ate, slept, made repairs, and even took time off to marry, raise crops, and families, and finally to die and be buried—all in the protected land that was part of the Great Wall system.

HOW IT BEGAN

The Great Wall is the most striking physical relic of a period of violent and sudden change. This was an upheaval which altered long-standing political and social relationships of the peoples of China. Previously, they had been divided peoples, subjects of separate feudal princes or dukes. No powerful single central government existed. These rulers of separate principalities or states sometimes warred among themselves. The victor then collected tribute from the loser, although it was always the feudal serfs who paid the bill in the end.

Repeatedly, nomad raiders from the north galloped southward in desperate attacks. The fertile lands of the feudal states drew them like a magnet. Some of the feudal dukes built towers or short sections of wall to defend their land against such attacks. It should be added that they built walls also to hold back possible onslaughts from their neighboring Chinese states. Walls were not proof against all attacks. Sooner or later a strong force could scale them, under-mine them, or batter gaps in them. At least they did slow up attackers, whether the barbarian nomads or the civilized feudal neighbors. Effective surprise attacks had to be made on horseback, and horses were hard to get over high walls!

In this period, disunity and danger went hand in hand. It was an era of petty principalities and incessant rivalries among princi-palities. In each of these almost-equal states, positions of power were hereditary. An able lord might be followed by a rash fool or an utter incompetent. Birth, rather than talent or training, dictated who should rule and who should obey and pay. The weaknesses of hereditary feudalism were woefully apparent.

About 235 B.C.E. a series of far-reaching and explosive changes began. The aggressive state of Ch'in, most northwesterly of all, was on the march. Its forces attacked, overwhelmed, and rapidly absorbed one after another of the neighboring states. Military genius of this historic conquest was the youthful Cheng, ruler of Ch'in. Ambitious and tireless, he wanted nothing less than absolute control of all territory where Chinese civilized agriculture was carried on.

By 221 B.C.E. Cheng had attained this goal. Rapidly and ruthlessly, he set about transforming his newly won territories. Traditional boundaries and differences were wiped out. The old dukedoms
were abolished. Instead, thiry-six districts were formed. Each was
governed by officers appointed by Emperor Cheng.

Thus, hereditary local rule and the feudal framework were eliminated. Great estates were broken up. Land was turned over to the
peasants who worked it. They paid high taxes directly to the new
central government. Step by step the Emperor enforced unity and
uniformity. His decrees established uniform weights and measures,
laws and regulations, throughout his realm. The separate fighting
forces of the old feudal lords were disarmed and disbanded. Their
members were told to become farmers.

In each district were stationed trained units of the Emperor's
standing army under commanders responsible directly to him.

This first imperial monarch of China forced masses of his subjects
to labor far from their home regions on great public works projects
and so tore apart established ties of clan, tribe, and home locality.
The great lines of power and decision now ran to and from the
elaborate palaces built in the new capital, later known as Hsianfu,
for the Emperor and his officers. There Cheng ruled, reading endless
reports, issuing decrees, and sometimes traveling out unannounced
and in disguise to see for himself what was happening throughout
his new empire.

Even the later Chinese historians, who hated his memory, could
not accuse him of being lax or lazy. His energy was astounding. He
was as fiercely determined to transform the newly unified land as
he had been to unify it by force of arms.

The evidence shows he knew well what he wanted and why.
He insisted on being known as an innovator. His breaks with tradition are hinted in the title he chose for himself, *Ch'in Shih Huang
Ti,* "first august sovereign of the Ch'in dynasty." The name China
itself may be traced to Ch'in. However, this was a name used by
the outside world. Later generations of educated Chinese did not
use it. They resented and despised the memory of Ch'in Shih
Huang Ti, for part of his effort to wipe out the past had been an

order to burn previous works of history. The scholars, whom he persecuted and punished, took revenge by blackening his memory. Historians of later epochs depicted him as a monster, bloodthirsty, superstitious, and mad.

His claims to greatness were inscribed at his order in public places during his lifetime: "He united the world for the first time." ("The world," of course, meant civilized, agricultural China—not the regions beyond where the barbarian nomads roamed.) "He has regulated and made equal the laws, the measures, and the standards for all . . . has brought order . . . has put an end to the battles." Another inscription boasted that the people now "enjoy calm and repose, arms are no longer necessary, and each man is peaceful in his dwelling."

Vast problems still plagued this forcibly unified and pacified new empire. Large numbers of people were without work or land or dwellings to be peaceful in. Vagrants, thieves, beggars, and destitute abounded. Hunger and unrest thus threatened from within. And from the north, beyond the lands suited for farming—remained the threat of the hard-hitting nomad raiders, probing and seeking to erupt anew into the fertile areas that drew them like magnets.

These barbarians were then called the *Hsiung-nu*. They were members of the same nomadic tribes who, later, as the Huns, plunged far westward, penetrating Italy itself under their famous leader, Attila. To push back the Hsiung-nu, the Emperor Ch'in Shih Huang Ti sent out a force of 300,000 men under Meng T'ien, a versatile and able commander. The apparent success of this drive prepared a basis for the most famous, and in many ways the most significant, decision ever made by this Emperor. He decided to use Meng T'ien and a massive army of workers to build a great defensive wall.


WHY THE GREAT WALL WAS NEEDED

The Wall has sometimes been pictured as a huge but hopeless attempt to pile up stone barriers against the movements of people and history. Fortified walls and towers today are outdated. Even

France's famous fortifications, the "Maginot Line," could not withstand in 1940 the weapons of modern mechanized lightning war. The Wall had many meanings about 2200 years ago: military, economic, social, and representative:

*Military*—It was planned to link together into an unbroken whole, existing bits and sections of wall that had been built by the feudal dukes and their vassals. The resulting system of structures could multiply the mobility and effectiveness of the border guards who had to be maintained.

*Economic*—As a vast public works project, it could employ many thousands of workers, increase the area of protected, arable land, and launch various new agricultural colonies along the inner line of the Wall.

*Social*—Masses of idle and restless people were taken from the towns and farming communities and kept at work under military supervision. The Wall was built largely by men who were otherwise likely to become a source of trouble.

*Representative*—The route chosen for the Wall was more than just a strategic line. It outlined and underscored the extent of the newly welded Empire. As a unified boundary marker of record length, it typified the passing of the former era of fragmented feudal principalities. It has been called "a symbol of China, the concrete and tangible representation of the unity of that vast land."

## THE MEANING OF THE WALL TODAY

Today we can regard the original Wall as a symbol of the sudden and sharp changes enforced by the extraordinary Ch'in Shih Huang Ti. Before him, it had been a divided land, parceled out among feudal princelings. In twenty years of imperial domination, Ch'in Shih Huang Ti stamped it with his pattern of centralized rule, a pattern strong enough to survive stresses and changes during more than twenty centuries that followed.

These facts lend fresh meaning to the Great Wall. It was not the first program of public works in China; irrigation systems, canals, and roads had been built before it. But it far exceeded them all in its physical scope and in its impact on great masses of people. The Great Wall, like other enormous structures of antiquity, was raised by hand. It consumed great amounts of labor. Chinese traditions tell of vast numbers of workers buried in or alongside the Wall, worn out by toil, and victims of accidents. To provide these battalions of manpower, prisons were emptied; vagrants, the homeless, and paupers were rounded up. Persons disliked or distrusted by the Emperor were marched off to work on the Wall. Troops of the imperial armies were assigned to assist or oversee the labor gangs.

Observers praised the perfect fit of stonework on completed sections of the Wall. Again, tradition has a gruesome explanation for this precision: an order that beheading should punish any stonemason who left between adjoining blocks of stone a gap big enough that a nail could be driven into it.

The entire main line of the Great Wall was certainly not completed during the lifetime of Ch'in Shih Huang Ti. The Emperor probably died in 283 B.C.E. when the actually completed stretches of Wall measured closer to 500 than to 1000 miles. But all subsequent extensions and supplements of the Great Wall were based on the over-all plan and the bold methods of construction that were applied or prepared for during his lifetime.

## HOW THE WALL WAS BUILT

Much of the Wall has been totally destroyed today. Other great stretches are terribly damaged. Probably nowhere could one find a substantial segment in its original state. Consequently, many questions about it remain without positive answers. Nevertheless, we can tell with fair certainty how the basic construction must have been planned, what the materials were, and what building methods were used.

The Wall had to be built to fit conditions and possibilities as they existed in different sections of the country. These conditions varied tremendously. If the various curving and looping lines of the Wall are traced from east to west across China, they can be divided roughly into three major segments.

(1) The most easterly section is the one most often pictured and described today. It begins near the shore of the Yellow Sea which is part of the Pacific Ocean, and curves westward, north of the great city of Peking, passing over hilly and mountainous terrain until it reaches the eastern branch of a great northward loop formed by the Hwang Ho (Yellow) River. This first section included about 800 miles of wall, or between forty and forty-five percent of the major wall structure.

(2) Between the eastern and western branches of the Yellow River loop, the Wall crosses the strange country whose soil is formed from the yellow silt, called *loess*. After this, the Wall forms a loop to the city of Lanchow. This entire section, including a total of about 600 miles of wall, represents more than thirty percent of the entire Great Wall system.

(3) The final segment runs from Lanchow, first in a northerly and then in a northwesterly direction, through mountainous country until the westernmost terminal point at Kiayukuan, or Kiuchuan. This final segment, with about 450 miles of wall, includes just less than one quarter of the major Wall structure.

Geography dictated choice of the locations that led to the Wall's sometimes confusing course on a map, with strange curves, loops, and gaps.

In the first segment, between the seacoast and its contact with the Yellow River, it was possible to jacket the Great Wall with stone and brick. Much of the stone came from quarries near Peking. Some, however, was taken from sources closer to the Wall section to which it was applied. These stone-brick portions are the most familiar. Photographs of them are common.

In the great second section, through the land of loess or silt, stone was not at hand. Here the Wall had to be formed mostly from the yellow-brown soil itself. In time, this part of the Wall came to resemble great mud ridges or mounds.

In the third section, through the province of Kansu and close to the southern border of Inner Mongolia, most of the Wall likewise came to resemble a muddy monster.

The probable sequence of buildings was: first, the free-standing or garrisoned towers; next, the wall-towers; and, finally, the Wall itself from wall-tower to wall-tower. In this way, the towers were completed first, to help protect the labor gangs against raids by the barbarians. The protective towers, once built, served as storehouses for food and supplies. The problem of feeding the army of laborers was enormous, especially in barren and isolated areas. Bandits still active inside the land added to the threat of nomad raids from the north. Many a convoy of food was lost before it could reach the Wall builders. Work did not go on at the same time all along the chosen line of the Wall. It began at selected supply centers and then spread out in both directions from each center. One report speaks of more than thirty such centers in use as Meng T'ien brought the project under way.

Once the wall-towers were in place, the next step was forming the foundations for the wall sections between. Two parallel deep ditches were dug, each about four feet wide and about fifteen to twenty-five feet apart. These were carried down to bedrock, if possible. Massive foundation blocks of granite were piled into the double trenches and were built up until they extended above the ground as high as a man or even higher.

On these stone foundations were laid two walls of brickwork, tapering as they rose. At a height of some eighteen to twenty feet above the ground, each wall was still between one and two feet thick. Now into the space between these two walls, masses of clay, soil, and boulders were packed. This fill was stamped down until the inside became like a single solid mass. Each wall was a sandwich of masonry, front and back, with packed earthwork and stone between.

The front wall was finished with a crenellated or notched top. This barrier, rising about six feet high, permitted archers and spearmen to fire through the gaps, yet remain protected against return missiles. Behind this protected firing line, a well-paved road ran along the top of the earth-fill. These wall-top roads were continuous. The towers, placed at intervals along the Wall, were pierced by large archways through which traffic traveled in both directions along the roads.

The Wall itself, once completed, provided its own protected highway for safe transport of manpower and materials. Troops, workers, stone, brick, food, and other essentials could move in safety to the next segments where construction was still under way.

Great care was taken to waterproof the surfaces of these wall-roads. They had ample drainage and the interior earth-fill was protected against damage from rainfall and melting snow. The towers, too, rising ten to twenty feet above the Wall itself, were built to withstand bad weather as well as barbarian foes.

All this exacting work was accomplished along a line that boldly climbs ridges, plunges down into valleys, and follows contours chosen for strategic defense rather than for ease of construction.

## THE WALL ACROSS THE LAND OF LOESS

In the loess-land, between the branches of the great hump of the Yellow River, very different kinds of wall-building had to be used. The labor gangs chopped away masses of the yielding and fertile yellow soil, leaving a great projecting ridge. This provided the earth-fill or core. Around this they built skins of bricks, or of stone, where that was available. For some stretches another technique was used. Frames or cribs were built of wood, and soft earth was compacted into them, rammed, and stamped down hard.

Today these more westerly sections of the Great Wall do not look as formidable and fortress-like as the great stone-and-brick constructions that lay east of the loop of the Yellow River. Mile after mile of wall took on the appearance described as "a heap of hard mud." In spite of this, an American who inspected stretches of the westernmost walls during the first decade of this century, found that in many places it still rose to heights of fifteen feet from a base fifteen feet thick, with intervening towers still thirty-five feet square at their bases and rising to heights of thirty feet.

Considering the enormous distances and difficulties, it is surprising how well these first Great Wall builders solved their many problems. The demands of the task were too great to be met simply by sending out supplies from existing towns and farming areas.

Armies of wall builders were set up in colonies at or near the major construction centers from which the Wall was to spread out. These colonies or settlements developed new irrigation and farmlands sufficient to supply basic food needs. The Emperor's armies protected them against barbarians, bandits, and against laziness in performing their assigned tasks.

As the crops began to come in, additional workers were added to the colony. Their wall-building became the major activity for most of the laborers, while a smaller number, very likely including their women, continued to plant, to cultivate, to harvest, and to prepare food.

In spite of its stupendous extent, the Great Wall may never have become more than a fraction of the full structure that Ch'in Shih Huang Ti intended. He has been credited with a truly titanic intention—to extend the Wall far toward the south, and then again to the east, thus forming it into a great arc whose two ends should touch the seacoast. In other words, a wall running completely around all the domain he had won and welded together. Had his doctors and magicians been able to bestow on him the endless life he craved, he might well have pressed on in his effort to extend the Wall around all the land boundaries of his realm.

## THE GREAT WALL REMAINS

The Wall as it stands today is the giant relic of an era when piled-up stones, bows and arrows, spears and swords might protect one group of men from attack by others. That era has vanished. Even in its heyday, the Great Wall was breached and penetrated time and again. Genghis Khan (1162–1227 c.e.) and his Mongol hordes were not the only barbarians who poured through the Wall as conquerors.

Modern maps show that the remains of the Wall no longer mark the northern limits of today's Chinese government whose red flag displays five stars. This new China comprises far more land and a vastly greater number of people than formed China in the eras when the Wall was built. The population controlled by the

People's Republic of China (*Chung-hua Jen-min Kung-ho Kuo*) now totals at least 750 million, may even exceed 800 million, and is rapidly increasing. This is a large fraction of the entire human race. Not only in numbers, but in economic installations, productivity, and military forces.

More than half a century ago, an energetic American explorer and geographer, William E. Geil, traveled far, tracing the Wall's surviving structures from end to end. Geil was well aware that the Wall meant more than just an ancient structure. He urged his fellow Americans to look at certain facts. As he was writing, the enormous construction of the Panama Canal was under way with the help of American-made power tools. The American press, he noted, was "in ecstasy" because on the Isthmus of Panama "a few billion cubic yards of earth are being moved."[6] Yet there had been no steam shovels or other power machinery to build the Great Wall of China and it had been impressively estimated that the Wall "took as much work as would have built all our railroads, all our canals, and nearly all our cities."

Before he began his explorations, Geil had found that the geography books, though they frequently mentioned the Great Wall, gave no clear answers to such questions as these: What is it made of? How long is it? How old is it? This situation seemed ridiculous to him, and he did much to remedy it. The lack of information about the Wall was part of a sweeping lack of information about all China. In fact, Geil observed, "We have an ignorance about China almost as colossal as that land."

In looking toward the future, Geil made some remarkable statements, based on his studies of the Great Wall. He noted that its originator, the Emperor Ch'in Shih Huang Ti, had been a unifier who "built roads over his new domains" and an innovator who had diminished the influence of the tradition-bound scholars and lifted the status of the farmers.

Then, Geil gave a warning that may seem prophetic in the light of events that, since his time, have transformed China. He reminded his fellow Americans that the land that had produced one Emperor Ch'in "may produce another." The first Ch'in had "built a wall to keep the foreigner out." Another and later Ch'in "may stride over that wall to put the foreigner in his proper place."

Even then, during the first decade of the present century, it was possible for an observer such as Geil to see in China that "the nation is astir and gaining momentum."

The Great Wall, then and in our own time, points toward the colossal forces of manpower and organized effort in the colossal land whose realities unfortunately have so often been walled off from us by a "colossal ignorance."

# VII

## THE COLOSSEUM OF ROME

## BLOODSTAINED SHOWPLACE
## OF CENTURIES

Type of the antique Rome! Rich reliquary
Of lofty contemplation left to Time
By buried centuries of pomp and power!

—Edgar Allan Poe, *The Coliseum* (sic)

"Stupendous" is a word often applied to this great structure in guidebooks and descriptions. "The greatest ruin of them all," is another typical phrase, along with "the most famous ruin" and "the pagan symbol of Rome's eternity." This is the *Colosseum* of Rome, or the Coliseum, as it is often spelled. It stands in majesty, enormous and enduring, though two thirds of its substance has been stripped away or stolen. Its battered arches and ravaged corridors, year after year, attract multitudes of visitors to busy, growing modern Rome. It is a symbol and a monument, both sacred and secular.

It was new nearly 1900 years ago. But in those days, citizens of Rome might have hesitated if asked, even in good Latin dialect, for directions to the Colosseum. If you asked instead where the gladiators would be fighting on the next holiday, their answers would be swift enough:

"Ah! In our great new *Flavian Amphitheater!*"

Three members of the Flavian clan, Vespasian and his sons Titus and Domitian, were responsible for the creation of this great building. Its enormous oval shape was formed by three layers of multiple arches, topped by a final section that towered 180 feet. The huge ellipse of the Colosseum measured about 620 feet long and 510 feet wide. Its circular seating of about 50,000 spectators was not exceeded until after the twentieth century began, when the Yale Bowl was built at New Haven, Connecticut.

The Colosseum was not the only site of the entertainments that the Roman masses craved and crowded to see. There were also theaters, seating from 8000 to 15,000. Here farcical comedies, satires, and sometimes tragedies were enacted; poetry was declaimed; or singing and instrumental music were performed.

In addition, there were the popular "circuses," designed mainly for chariot races. Giant among these was the Circus Maximus, dating from about 250 B.C.E. As many as 300,000 people could sit or stand beside its great track, more than 1800 feet long and 600 feet wide. They shouted and screamed with excitement while their favorite drivers urged two-horse or four-horse teams seven times around the course. The chariot races were hard fought, often dangerous. The Roman chariot-race fans awaited them eagerly, applauded, or jeered wildly, and relived every detail for days afterward.

None of these amusements could compete with those in the Colosseum. The combat shows served up in the Colosseum were most typical of the prevalent taste and brutality of Rome during its centuries as ruling center of a far-flung empire. Such games became increasingly prominent in the period of outward glory and inner moral decline that began around 30 B.C.E. when Augustus became the first *princeps,* or emperor. That era reached a symbolic close just about 500 years later in 476 C.E. It was then that the last Roman emperor of the west was deposed and a non-Roman— a barbarian mercenary soldier named Odovacer—took the throne, as king of Italy.

Rome had been ruled as a republic, in name at least, prior to Augustus. Under his lengthy rule, and for long afterwards, many of the traditions and outward forms of the Republic were retained. There was still the Senate, composed of heads of great landowning families. The Senators went through formalities of selecting, confirming, sometimes even of deposing the emperor-princeps.

But under the Republic there had been open debate and decision on important questions of public policy. Now, in the era of the emperors, decisions were made mostly in secret by the powerful princeps and a few close to him. Cliques and conspiracies, not the open debate of political opponents, decided the vital policies of Rome, the world power.

## BREAD AND CIRCUSES

More and more, the Roman masses were cut off from political participation, influence, freedom of action, and independent means of livelihood. To substitute for this lack of true citizenship, the state supplied "bread and circuses." "Bread" referred to huge imports of grain and other necessities from the empire outside Rome, supplied to its people at low prices or even without cost. "Circuses" meant the races, the shows, and, above all, the bloody games—mostly offered free—for which the Colosseum was created.

In many such spectacles, wild beasts, first goaded to fury, attacked and destroyed one another. In others, armed men hunted down and slew beasts—if they could. In still others, armed fighters, or gladiators, battled till the loser was helpless. Then, if the audience called for it, the victor finished off the loser with a final sword-thrust.

The Colosseum did not originate these bloody spectacles. It simply provided them with a bigger, more elaborate setting. Captives of war, condemned criminals, and slaves had been forced to fight to the death in public shows as early as 350 years before the Colosseum was first opened to the public in 80 c.e.

The bloody destruction of animals by other animals or by men began to be a regular Roman amusement or recreation about 250 years before there was a Colosseum. It may have been an outgrowth of less bloody public displays of wild beasts brought back from the far corners of Rome's expanding empire.

Cruelty and blood-lust were strong in the people, most of them poor and many destitute, who lived in slums near the luxuries and grandeurs of imperial Rome. Staging such deadly displays became an accepted, even an expected, way to win popularity. Politicians seeking public approval and votes, paid for such games. Their henchmen and supporters handed out the ivory tickets to Roman citizens. Generals of the army, eager for advancement and acclaim, brought back to Rome thousands of captives to fight as gladiators and countless wild beasts to tear or be torn to bits.

These variety shows of mutilation and destruction included animals from many far places made tributary to Rome: lions, tigers, leopards, bears, hyenas, wild horses and asses, zebras, elephants, giraffes, hippopotamuses, and even a rhinoceros now and then. Bull-fighting is said to have been introduced to the Roman mob in an entertainment staged by Julius Caesar, not long before the era of the Roman emperors began. Spectacles such as these, compounded of danger, courage, and bestial cruelty have survived a long time in our civilized world.

## FORERUNNERS OF THE COLOSSEUM

Until about 30 B.C.E., such deadly games of men, beasts, and blood were watched by Roman crowds from temporary stands and seats put up for the occasion and removed again after the last bleeding carcass had been dragged away. In that year the city's first permanent amphitheater, partly of stone, partly of wood, was erected. Though soon too small for the mobs who sought to see the games, it was a genuine *amphi-theatrum* (amphi—on both sides, or around) because the seats for the spectators ran all the way around the inner arena. Thus it differed from the ordinary Roman *theatrum* where audiences sat in a semicircle, facing the stage on which actors performed.

Many bloody games were staged in this first amphitheater. The taste for bloodshed intensified with time. The power, the wealth, the pomp, and the imperial plunder of Rome were interlocked with these hideous, inhuman amusements or distractions. Any picture of Roman life that hides these horrors is, unfortunately, false or incomplete.

The first amphitheater was still the setting for such games in 54 C.E. In that year, a neurotic young man named Nero became emperor. He proved to be vain, vicious, willful, and unstable. Seeking a sense of security that always eluded him, he sought enormous luxury, theatrical display, and the applause of the people.

Nero's actions and antics enraged more and more of the aristocrats who made up the traditional Roman Senate. Several later historians, who shared their attitude, pictured Nero as a depraved monster who deliberately set fire to Rome, then played on his fiddle or harp while it burned. Afterward, they charged, he blamed the crime on the new sect of Christians, whom he persecuted with fiendish torture.

Much of Rome was destroyed in 64 C.E. by a devastating fire that started at the Circus Maximus. Whether Nero did or did not instigate the blaze, he welcomed the opportunity it provided later on—to rebuild much of Rome anew, and thus to glorify himself by glorifying his capital city.

Nero poured out great sums to build public baths, a gymnasium, and a new amphitheater to replace the one destroyed in the fire. However, Nero's new site for gladiatorial games was made of wood and was not likely to endure long.

Most costly and flaunting was the palace and pleasure estate that Nero built for himself and his favorites. Called "Nero's House of Gold," it spread over a broad area that had previously been city land. Many slum dwellings had previously stood there. It appeared that the great emperor had ousted the poor to make room for his private pleasures and display.

Beside a variety of richly decorated rooms both above and below ground, the Golden House displayed two prominent features. One was an artificial lake for the Emperor's private pleasure; the other was a colossal statue sculpted in gilt bronze by Zenodorus, a leading artist of the day. It stood well over 100 feet tall—some say even over 200 feet.

In front of the Golden House, it loomed, its face and head unmistakably those of Nero. Sunlike rays in a halo radiated above the brow. It was a Roman way of telling the world that Nero was a deity, sharing the divinity of the sun god, Phoebus Apollo.

Romans soon called this pompous statue "the Colossus," the name of a famous image, one of the seven wonders of the ancient world that was said to have stood astride the entrance to the harbor at Rhodes.

The real Nero, no giant or god but a very weak human cursed with excessive power, could not stay quiet in his Golden House beside the man-made lake. His need to show off and win applause drove him constantly to the chariot races. He even competed in them and, though he did poorly, was naturally declared victor.

Probably even more shocking to the Roman patricians were Nero's appearances on theater stages as a common actor and singer, seeking the applause of his subjects in the audiences. He composed songs or poetry, and performed them himself. No powerful Roman, it seemed, had ever gone so far to cater to the crowd's love of shows.

Although Nero's private life was stained with murder and brutality, he did oppose the cruelest excesses of the public gladiatorial games. He decreed that such fights should not be carried all the way to the death of the losers.

Senatorial opposition to Nero grew. Finally, the emperor's own military elite, the Praetorian guard stationed in Rome, turned against him. The senators named a new emperor to replace him. Alone, abandoned by former followers and favorites, faced by a terrible death if captured, Nero managed to commit suicide.


EMPEROR AFTER EMPEROR

In swift and shocking succession, Rome was ruled by three short-time emperors—Galba, Otho, and Vitellius—all within a year and a half. Each was slaughtered miserably by supporters of his successor. The civil warfare devastated great sections of Rome itself.

Now the Senate called to the post of power Vespasian, a very different man. Their call had to go all the way to far off Judaea, the Roman name for the land of the Jews. The Jewish population had rebelled against their Roman overlords and army of occupation. Vespasian, as commander of Roman armies in that part of the empire, was trying to stamp out this stubborn revolt.

Vespasian, aged 60, was a blunt, realistic, hard-bitten campaigner. His plebeian birth and the cruel work he had done for the Roman empire had schooled and toughened him. He knew that, though emperor, he would be no god-on-earth. He turned over to his son, Titus, the task of subduing the rebellious Jews, and returned to rule and to win over Rome.

Vespasian ruled with canny good sense from 70 to 79 C.E. He died while in office, regretted by most of the influential elements of Rome. While he lived, his economies and energetic tax policies poured funds into his treasuries. These funds he spent not on private luxury, but largely on reconstruction and additions for Rome.

He commanded that rubble be cleared away and damaged structures he restored. Also, this long-time soldier raised a new shrine in Rome—to Pax, as the beneficent goddess of peace was called in Latin.

While he avoided wars on the outskirts of the empire, Vespasian knew how to appeal to the rootless and sensation-hungry masses in

Rome, both the few who had so much wealth they did not need to work, and the many who had neither wealth nor work to do. Plans were prepared at his command for a new, permanent amphitheater of a size beyond anything ever attempted.

The site chosen was symbolic—where once Nero's private lake had stood beside the opulent "House of Gold." In a way, Vespasian was returning to the Romans the municipal land that Nero had taken for his private extravagances.

Vespasian saw to it that his "Flavian Amphitheater" would surpass all before it. The most skilled architects of Rome worked out a bold design. It still wins admiration from engineers today. As the first rings of eighty great stone arches began to rise, Romans realized that it was to be enormous.

Architects, overseers, carpenters, stonemasons, workers in concrete, and other craftsmen now swarmed where once the waters of Nero's private lake had rippled in the breezes of Rome. Slaves, as usual, did much of the roughest labor. Near them worked gangs of Rome's impoverished freemen—the property-less and usually jobless class to whom the name *proletariat* was given.

Building of the Colosseum was barely started when a typical Roman triumphal parade was staged to glorify Titus, son of the Emperor. He had returned victorious at last, after years of difficult efforts to crush rebellion in Judaea. With him he brought great gangs of Jewish prisoners to Rome. Some were thrown to the wild beasts or gladiators in the victory games. Others were set to labor as slaves of the lowest sort.

Most spectacular among the tasks forced on these slaves was work on the new amphitheater. Just how much of that building they did, we cannot be certain now. The tradition is, however, quite definite. Thus, Bernard Postal and S. H. Abramson write about the Colosseum, "Jewish prisoners brought to Rome after the fall of Judaea were employed in its construction."[7]

Quite likely their labor continued even after it was first opened to the public of Rome in 80 c.e. The great triumphal arch erected to honor Titus in the Forum of Rome, was completed after his death in 81 c.e. W. T. Field tells how each morning Jewish slaves, marched from filthy quarters in their segregated (ghetto) section to their tasks at the Colosseum, had to pass this arch "which celebrated their degradation."[8]

"It is not strange," Field adds, "that they came to hate the arch so completely that not one of them would pass beneath it"—unless forced to do so.

More than eighteen centuries later, however, a company of Jewish soldiers did march under the Arch of Titus. It was at a very different victory celebration—celebrating the liberation of Rome from German and Italian Fascists in World War II. These marchers were the Jewish Brigade, composed of volunteers from Palestine. And this victory procession was said to "symbolize the rebirth of the people whom Titus believed he had destroyed forever."

## THE COLOSSEUM CONTINUES TO GROW

Titus ruled as princeps, or Emperor as we would call it, less than two years. He was followed by Domitian, another son of Vespasian, in a reign that lasted from 81 C.E. until cut short by assassination in 96 C.E.

During his years as princeps, Domitian pushed ahead with extensive and costly building programs that had been launched under Vespasian and Titus. These included important additions to the great Flavian amphitheater. The Colosseum was thus originally constructed under three successive emperors of the Flavian clan.

Finally, many years after it was begun, the great showplace was completed. Now its three underlying levels of arches were topped by the lofty rim, already mentioned. This was in the form of a wall, pierced at intervals by square, windowlike openings. This rim added nearly 40 percent to the previous height of the Colosseum. It represented a new and daring trend in Roman design.

## CONSTRUCTION OF THE COLOSSEUM

The ruins that loom so large in Rome today reveal many details of the clever inner construction of this Flavian amphitheater. Its basic units of strength and support were Roman arches by the hundreds. Easily visible still are evidences of the three exterior layers, or stories, each formed by a ring of eighty great arches. They were stacked one above the other, 240 exterior arches in all.

The arches on the ground level served as entrances and exits, leading to the interior of the Colosseum. There were four principal portals, and more than seventy numbered tunnel entrances. So carefully had the entrance-exit pattern been prepared that the filled Colosseum could be emptied in about ten minutes.

Roman construction leaned heavily on masonry arches. Sometimes it seemed as if Roman architects could never include enough arches. A well-built stone arch allows heavy weight to be borne by supports set much further apart than columns in the Greek type of building, which holds up a horizontal beam or lintel by means of pillars set at rather frequent intervals. (The Parthenon provides a famous illustration of this.)

Under its fine limestone skin, the Colosseum was supported by a skeleton composed of a network of more than 1000 arches. Beside the 240 exterior arches already mentioned, there were an additional 720 major arches of comparable size within. They were placed in two great systems: the concentric and the radial arches.

The major concentric arches were set in elliptical rings. Three such rings could be seen from the outside. Three more rings were set within these. There were 480 ring arches in all.

The major radial arches were set in lines that fanned out, as if pointing away from the central point of the ellipse, in the middle of the arena. There were eighty such radial arch systems on each of the three lower levels. The lowest had three arches in line, the next higher two arches, and the third level, only one arch. Thus, there were six times eighty major radial arches, or 480 radial arches.

The great arches that formed the inner skeleton of the Colosseum thus totaled 480 in the rings, 480 in the radials, or 960 together. They were built of rocks cut from a porous limestone called *tufa,* clamped together by metal hoops and hooks.

Tufa was chosen for strength and relative lightness, not display. Outside surfaces were covered with a firmer, more closely knit limestone rock called *travertine,* much more pleasing to the eye and better able to withstand weather.

On top of this basic inverted cone formed from mighty arches were locked a vast number of minor arches made of concrete. These provided direct supports for the stepped-back elliptical rings of seats.

The Colosseum structure, itself, was designed as an ingenious system of entrance-exits, vaulted tunnels, and stairways. On both its second and third stories, the Colosseum showed a cross-vaulting construction unknown in earlier Roman structures. Here too it blazed trails that led later architects to new designs.

Concrete, that durable artificial stone formed by men, often seems a modern building material. However, the Colosseum abounded in carefully constructed concrete arches, vaultings, supports, and other details.

To keep the great seating sections as light as possible, the concrete of the Colosseum was the type called "pumice stone concrete." Lime was combined with a porous volcanic ash material called *pozzolana*. This made the cement, into which the bulky aggregate of stone and rock fragments was mixed. When this mixture hardened in its forms, it became very durable and resistant to wear.

This Roman-style cement helped the Colosseum survive several major earthquakes and repeated vandalism and civil warfare in Rome. The structure might still appear almost complete, had it not been systematically plundered. It was used as a "quarry" from which vast numbers of stones were stripped to build churches and private palaces in Rome during the sixteenth and seventeenth centuries.

The resulting façade produced an effect that is described in *The Cambridge Ancient History* as "probably still the most imposing symbol and monument"[9] of the Roman imperial majesty. The Colosseum now towered to "a fantastic and dizzy height."

Among the many Roman amphitheaters in other cities or towns of the empire, none attempted or achieved anything comparable to this Colosseum. Architecturally, it represented, according to the work mentioned, "the ultimate stage of romanization."

The Colosseum's lofty wall section was more than an innovation. It also helped to complete and unify a structure that without it might have seemed simply three repeating tiers of arches. The exterior was knit together by the use of so-called "pilasters" placed in front of the eighty pillars on which the arches rested at each level.

A pilaster is a dummy column, emerging partly from a wall or support behind it. Its aim is to contribute to the appearance, not to the actual support. The completed circumference of the Colosseum showed eighty stacks, or sets, of four pilasters, one above the other. Their styles were derived from Greek art, as was much else in Roman culture.

The pilasters mounted on the lowest, or ground, level of arches are in the simplest Greek style, called *Doric*. Those on the second level are in a more elaborate style called *Ionic*. And those at the highest level of arches are in the still more ornate *Corinthian*, a style more Roman than Greek. The pilasters of the first three levels were rounded. Those of the added wall section above were rectangular projections. All of them terminated in the traditional ornamented tops, or capitals.

Thus, by means of the lines of these superimposed pilasters, the observer's eye was drawn from the ground upward toward the top. As a result the completed Colosseum stressed the vertical and upward feeling, and escaped the squat horizontal effect of a mere series of arcades, stacked one on top of the other.

## THE COLOSSEUM AND THE COLOSSUS

The effect of "fantastic and dizzy height" accounts for the use of the name *Colosseum* rather than *Amphitheatrum Flavium*. It rose near that huge statue, the Colossus, that Nero had built to show Rome that he was a god. Nero's head no longer topped this statue—a head of the sun-god Phoebus Apollo had been substituted. But it was still "the Colossus" to the Romans. Almost inevitably, the towering new amphitheater was associated with the towering statue, and so the *Amphitheatrum* became the *Colosseum*.

Today the world has other coliseums, but only the one *Colosseum* —and it is the most readily recognized single structure in all Rome, possibly in all Italy or even all Europe.

Outside, the Colosseum was original and unforgettable. Inside too was unique. Every trick of Roman design was used so that the

Colosseum's shows would appear more surprising, sensational, and shocking than those elsewhere in the civilized and bloodthirsty world of that time.

An amphitheater, essentially, is a suitable seating arrangement around an *arena*. That Roman name comes from the word for sand, its covering substance, which could be quickly changed to hide spilt blood and mangled flesh.

In this great arena, the sand was spread over a stout floor of planks. These hid a complex system of underground chambers, tunnels, dens, and drains. Wild beasts were driven through protected passageways into chosen dens under the arena floor. Then they could be raised quickly by means of an elevator-like hoist or a ramp plus trapdoor to the arena itself, ready to face their prey, or their pursuers. As Donald R. Dudley, an acute historian of Roman history, has written, it was the Colosseum that "gave 50,000 people their regular ration of sadism."

The stage management of a full show, starting about ten o'clock in the morning and continuing into the afternoon, was no simple matter. The crowds became critical, demanding new and more gruesome spectacles. By this period, most of them never bore arms themselves, but as the author Will Durant has pointed out, in the Colosseum they could be brave by proxy, feeling as if they had run risks in that arena from which they were so safely separated.

## PROTECTING THE SPECTATORS

The wall around the arena was fully fifteen feet high, arranged so even the fiercest tiger or lion could not scramble up in an effort to attack, or escape. Armed guards were stationed for added protection.

At the top of that surrounding wall were the choicest places, on a broad platform called the *podium*. Here, on elegant chairs or couches, reclined the greats of Rome: the Emperor, his family, leading Senators, and other selected persons.

They had an unrestricted view of the blood, sweat, and carnage. And it was here that the gladiators, before attacking each other, were required to assemble to give their ironic salute to the Emperor: "Hail, Caesar! Those about to die salute you!"

Behind and above the podium, the great oval funnel formed by the multirowed seats of the Colosseum sloped upward. The lower the seating level, the higher the social standing of its occupants, and vice versa. Thus, the first fourteen rows were reserved for the equestrian or knightly class, the aristocracy of Rome. Beyond and above, were twenty-two additional rows of seats for free Romans of lesser birth and family status.

After these select rows, there was a wall. Beyond and above that rose the gallery—about twelve rows of supplementary seats, far from the arena—for the mere plebeians, the aliens, and such slaves or other riffraff as managed to get tickets.

Thus, the men of Rome were ranked by their classes, here as elsewhere in their lives. The word "men" is used deliberately: few women were permitted to attend. They came only from the social extremes: ladies of the imperial or other highest families, and per-haps some Vestal Virgins, at or near the podium; and, up at the top, perhaps forced to stand or lean, a few women of the lower classes. Doubtlessly, they screamed, cheered, or jeered as frantically as the men about them.


THE INLAND SEA BATTLES

Sometimes, for a change, the oval arena was partly filled with water. In this synthetic sea, naval battles were staged. Not harmless sham fights, but deadly struggles between boats rowed by slaves and manned by marine gladiators. They slashed, stabbed, and drowned their opponent, if they could, before he did it to them. With luck, one or two might survive, to fight another day.

Arrangements for rapidly filling and draining the arena were among the admired engineering features of the Colosseum.

Considering the tight, hand-to-hand fights it presented, and the lack of modern telescopes or field glasses in that era, the Colosseum was just about as big as was feasible in its time. Spectators further from the arena than those at its uppermost rim, would have had to strain to make out who was killing and who was being killed.

## FAMILIAR SURVIVALS FROM THE COLOSSEUM

Basically, the Colosseum was constructed as an interlocked system of vaulting arches and hollow shells. An American accustomed to finding his seat at football games or trackmeets in a modern concrete-and-steel amphitheater such as the Los Angeles Memorial Coliseum (with a seating capacity double that of the old Roman amphitheater) would probably have found himself more or less at home in the latter—as soon as he learned to read the Roman numerals on his ivory ticket.

If he had been invited to sit near the Emperor on the *podium* he would have entered one of the four major portals. Otherwise, he would have entered one of more than seventy arches on the ground level, as his ticket indicated. By taking the correct turn in the tunnel, he would come to his designated stairway, leading up and into the interior of the great funnel, near his assigned seat.

A passageway leading from a landing inside the Colosseum was called, quite vividly, a *vomitorium*. There were 160 of these, so if the crowd numbered 48,000, an average of about 300 spectators left the amphitheater by means of each vomitorium. If each exit let out as many as thirty persons per minute, the entire audience could surely be out and away within that ten-minute period.

The hot Roman sun blasted down on the Colosseum during many a bloody holiday. Enormous awnings could be spread to shade the lower tiers of seats. Skilled sailors, stationed in Rome for the purpose, spread and adjusted these great awnings. But the lower classes, seated higher, were permitted to sweat without shade.

## THROUGH THE CENTURIES

The Colosseum remained the outstanding showplace for what W. T. Field described as "the most terribly realistic tragedy ever presented for the entertainment of mankind."[10] Edward Gibbon wrote of "the inhuman sports of the amphitheater."[11]

Some Romans apparently attended so regularly that they gained, or claimed, rights to particular seats, even in the stone-carved benches where the upper classes sat. Hundreds of them carved their names, possibly during a lull between battles, to identify their places. A couple of hundred such name carvings have been found in the incomplete Colosseum that survives.

Tale after tale about the Colosseum has been handed down. Emperors, ambitious politicians, and rich men seeking to curry favor, repeatedly staged huge displays of wild beasts and bestialized men. Gladiators more than once rebelled against their terrible fate. Some attempted desperately to break out of their cages. Others committed suicide in groups, by mutual agreement, rather than slay each other in public to amuse the screaming, sweating Roman crowds.

Most common among the tales and legends are those that concern the martyred Christians who died by imperial order in the Colosseum. Such a scene was envisaged by Field in this way: ". . . to the intense delight of the spectators a company of Christians are thrown in, to fight or be destroyed. Then the beasts are killed by a horde of attendants and, when the butchery is over, the multitude, drunk with the sight of blood, more savage than the beasts themselves, rush out through the *vomitoria,* and the Colosseum is deserted."[12]

Christianity made headway in the Roman world, gained toleration, and finally acceptance. Yet even this change did not bring an immediate end to the Colosseum's gruesome games. Among the relatively few educated Romans there were some who privately expressed distaste for the slaughter of men and beasts, but it stubbornly remained part of the established way of life and death in the imperial city, while the fabric and morale of Rome continued to decay.

Disgust and denunciation became more effective toward the close of the fourth century C.E. Finally, about the year 404 an edict was issued banning the gladiatorial combats to the death. The goading, hunting, and slaughter of animals, however, continued to provide public spectacles during more than a century after that date.

In spite of earthquakes and social upheavals, the great strength of the Colosseum appears to have preserved it relatively complete until about the mid-sixteenth century. After that, during the greater part of two centuries it was systematically "mined" as a source of stone for newer building in the Eternal City, which was then ruled by the popes.

The nephews of Pope Paul III tore away great segments to use in building their Farnese Palace. The powerful family of the Barberini also took much material for their palace. Other mansions in which parts of the Colosseum appeared included the palazzi called di Venezia and della Cancelleria. Still other parts of its substance were taken to build the great papal basilica or church of St. Peter, now part of Vatican City.

No wonder the present Colosseum ruin includes barely one third of the material in the original structure. Even this surviving remnant might have vanished, had not a halt finally been called in the middle of the eighteenth century. Pope Benedict XIV then formally dedicated it to be a holy place, sanctified by the blood of Christian martyrs. After that, a cross stood in what had been the principal arena of the pagan world.

# VIII

## THE CHURCH OF SANTA SOPHIA

---

## BEAUTY FROM BYZANTIUM

Justinian cried: "Glory be to God, who has
judged me worthy of accomplishing such a
work as this! O Solomon, I have outdone you!"

—AT DEDICATION OF SANTA SOPHIA, 537

In Istanbul, Turkey, once known to the world as Constantinople, stands the most magnificent example of the flowering of Byzantine art. It is the Church of Santa Sophia, built by the Emperor Justinian in 532–537 C.E.

Istanbul's physical location overlooking the Bosphorus with Asia on the far side, its exotic mosques and minarets, its many hills and beautiful vistas, make it an extraordinary setting for this great jewel of Byzantine architecture. Aside from its aesthetic importance, Santa Sophia's history is closely bound, not only to that of the city of Constantinople, but also to the political and religious history of the entire Roman Empire. In addition, it had a significant role in the development of the Christian Church and that body's eventual division into the rival Roman and Greek Orthodox Catholic churches. Santa Sophia, as it is known to most Westerners, was not named for any saint. Called Hagia Sophia, Agia Sophia, or Aya Sofya in the East, its name means Holy Wisdom or Divine Wisdom or the "Creative Logos of God Himself." It was once known simply as "The Great Church."

## THE HISTORY OF BYZANTIUM

In about 657 B.C.E., a group of Greek colonists founded a town on the Bosphorus and called it Byzantium. The name of this settlement endured for a thousand years and has lived to this day as the designation of a particular art and civilization. The Bosphorus connects the city to the Sea of Marmara on the west and the Black Sea on the east, ringing the town on three sides by water and making it almost impregnable. Its harbor, the Golden Horn, called "Keras" (horn) by the Greeks because of its shape, and "golden" to suggest the wealth of its trade, is an inlet of the Bosphorus. Here fleets of war ships and trading and fishing vessels found refuge from attack and storm.

For about 100 years after the Emperor Marcus Aurelius' death in 180 C.E., the Roman Empire was beset by a long series of external and civil wars, plagues, and famines. In an attempt to restore a dying empire, Diocletian, who became emperor in 283 C.E., divided it into two parts, the Eastern and Western sections, each under a separate *Augustus*. The division was one of theory, rather than fact, and proved unsuccessful. It was united finally, once more, under Constantine, who became the sole Augustus. In the east the Persians were causing trouble for the Empire, and Constantine decided to make his headquarters there rather than in Rome.

Byzantium, because of its strategic position, was chosen as the new capital and Constantine proceeded to rebuild it on a grand scale. He called the reconstructed city "New Rome," dedicating it on May 11, 330, but the people named it "Constantinople," to honor the man who had reunited the empire and erected this magnificent new capital. Constantinople remained its name for some 1600 years until, in 1930, the Turkish Government officially renamed it Istanbul.

Constantine was friendly and sympathetic toward the Christians, reversing the attitude of previous emperors. He encouraged the construction of churches and for one of these a site was chosen on a hill in the northeast section of the city. The resulting church was called Santa Sophia and was built of stone and wood. Before he died, Constantine changed his religion and became the first Christian Emperor of Rome.

A hundred years later, during a political upheaval, this first Church of Santa Sophia was destroyed by fire. It was rebuilt by Theodosius the Great (c. 346–395) under whom the Roman Empire was divided once more into two parts, the Western section with its capital in Rome, the Eastern centered in Constantinople. The division this time was permanent. For about the next thousand years, Constantinople was to remain the most beautiful, most civilized, and the richest city in the world.

On the other hand, within less than seventy-five years after the death of Constantine in 337 C.E., the Western empire under Rome had begun its decline and by the latter part of the fifth century, a vassal king of Italy became subordinate to the emperor at Constantinople.

## JUSTINIAN

In the sixth century, the Christian Emperor Justinian, determined to make Constantinople the most magnificent of cities, began one of the most ambitious building programs in history. This was the period in which Greek, Roman, Oriental, and Christian influences fused into the creation of what is now called Byzantine art.

Justinian's expansion policy placed severe taxation burdens and heavy manpower demands on the people. These were aggravated by growing discontent over disputes within the Christian church. Two opposing factions, formerly "sports" groups supporting different teams of chariot racers whose games were held in the "Circus" or "Hippodrome," developed into active political parties and joined forces. Their object was to dethrone the emperor. In January, 532, the historic Nika revolt broke out. Shouting "Nika!" (conquer!), their rallying cry, the people rioted, storming and burning buildings. Santa Sophia was burned to the ground and 30,000 citizens of Constantinople lost their lives. The ambitious, persistent Theodora, Justinian's wife, persuaded the emperor to hold firm and the riot was quelled by the prompt action of his commander-in-chief, Belisarius.

Justinian was then faced with the task of rebuilding the city. This meant further increases in taxation, but brought about the transformation of Santa Sophia into one of the most magnificent buildings in the world. All the building resources of the state were concentrated on reconstructing the Church of Holy Wisdom so that it could be completed quickly. More than ten thousand skilled workmen, brought from virtually all over the known world, labored under the direction of a hundred master builders. These workmen were paid in pieces of fine silver every day after work. Historians have estimated the cost of building to have been 320,000 pounds of gold, an enormous sum for those days, and one which drained the treasury. Justinian, clad in white linen tunic, visited the site constantly, offering advice, encouraging the workers and rewarding them for skill and speed.

The new church was completed in just five years, eleven months, and ten days after it was started. At the dedication on December 26, 537, Justinian, raising his arms to heaven, cried, "Glory to God, who has judged me worthy of accomplishing such a work as this! O Solomon, I have outdone you!"

Edward Gibbon, writing of Justinian, said the finished church "remains . . . a stately monument of his fame."[13]

## THE "DOME ON PENDENTIVES"

To design Santa Sophia, Justinian brought from Greece, Anthemius of Tralles, the greatest architect of his day. Anthemius' architect nephew, Isidorus of Miletus, an early scientist, worked as his uncle's assistant. Anthemius has been described by an early writer as "the man most skilled in the mathematical sciences not only of his own day, but of all time."

The most important architectural significance of Santa Sophia arises from the fact that it marked the first successful attempt to place a circular dome on a square building, "the dome on pendentives."

The central section of the building was built as a square whose sides were approximately 120 feet long. Huge columns, 100 feet high, were placed in each corner. Connecting the tops of these columns were four great arches, sixty feet in radius. On top of these arches was placed the dome.

When earlier Roman builders had tried to put a circular dome onto a square building, the lower part of the dome, touching the square only at midpoints, had left great gaps. These gaps had been filled in, however, in a most unsatisfactory and slipshod manner.

But in Santa Sophia, the dome now rested on the tops of the four arches which spanned the columns. To fill the spaces left between the horizontal edge of the dome and the curving vertical of the arches on which it rested, the "pendentives" were inserted. These were triangular forms of masonry, whose apexes pointed downward, their bowed sides clinging to the curves of the arches beside them, and their bases, above, arching to meet the lower rim of the dome. Forty arched windows circled the dome at its base, lessening its weight and adding to the beautiful lighting of the church interior.

The dome itself first was made very shallow, only about 26 feet high, but its outward thrust proved too great, and its eastern section collapsed on May 7, 558, as the result of an earthquake. By this time, Anthemius, the architect, was dead, but the dome was rebuilt some twenty feet taller by Isidorus. It now rose some 46 feet above its base, but was still surprisingly low for its span, for it had a diameter of 120 feet. The distance from the floor of the church to the ceiling of the dome was approximately 200 feet, the equivalent of a sixteen-story building. In spite of its great height and unbelievable span, the dome gave the impression of incredible delicacy. It was built of lightweight pumice-stone and bricks especially chosen for lightness.

The early historian, Procopius, in his description of Santa Sophia, said of the dome that it "does not appear to rest upon a solid foundation, but to cover the place beneath it as though it were suspended from heaven by a fabled golden chain. All the parts are surprisingly joined to one another in the air, are suspended from one another and rest only on that which is next to them, and form the work into one admirably harmonious mass."[14]


THE INTERIOR OF SANTA SOPHIA

The frame of the building as a whole was made of brickwork, surfaced by marble. Between the huge corner columns and under the great arches on the north and south sides of the church, stood rows of smaller columns in two tiers, one above the other, with their fitting arches. On the exterior of these sides, tremendous buttresses formed the support between the walls and the foundations. Marble for the building was brought from the Proconnesian island in the Sea of Marmara, while many columns incorporated in the church came from plundered temples not only in Asia Minor but also to the west as far as the Atlantic shores.

On the east and west sides of the church, the space between the soaring corner columns was left open, and the church was extended here by means of semicircular walls covered with half-domes above. These half-domes served to roof the nave and chancel of the church, while their exteriors were used to brace the huge main arches of the building.

Under the great dome and the smaller half-domes, the floor, from east to west, thus took the shape of a huge rectangle with curved ends, and the shape of the church itself, that of a Greek cross within a quadrangle. The four arms of the Greek cross are all equal in length.

The nave or body of the church, where the worshipers gathered was divided from the choir by a balustrade on one side of which was the throne of the emperor, on the other that of the patriarch (the spiritual head of the Greek Orthodox Church corresponding to the pope in the Roman Catholic Church).

Three aisles, or immense chambers, made up the interior of the church. The largest, the central section, took shape between the four corners formed by the huge columns. This provided sufficient area for large congregations. Above were the galleries where the royal families and their attendants had their places during ceremonies in the church. Upper and lower galleries were assigned to women who were separated from the men at times of worship, as in the Hebrew orthodox temples. To the west was the main entrance, whose bronze doors still survive. In the northeast section stood a circular treasury, and near the southwest corner, a square baptistry.

Real gold, in the form of thin sheets, covered the ceiling, while beautiful marbles in dozens of colors brought from every part of the Roman Empire, made up the pavement, walls, and colonnades. Marble, jasper, and porphyry were skillfully used and blended. Brilliant mosaics added to the splendor of the church.

Behind the pulpit, whose sides were decorated in silver plaques and had steps inlaid with ivory, was a huge cross set with precious stones. Precious metals were used abundantly. Paul Silentarius, the poet, wrote that the silver in the sanctuary alone weighed 40,000 pounds, and that the vases and decorations of the altar were of gold. The altar itself, shaped in a semicircle, was in the eastern recess. Doors led from there to the sacristy, the vestry, and the baptistry. Capitals, arches, moldings, and cornices were covered with delicate stone carvings in the classic shapes of leaves.

The writers of the day were ecstatic. So unusual and overwhelming was the effect of the light caused by the placement of its many windows in the dome and the galleries, that it drew from Procopius the statement that it was so "singularly full of light and sunshine that you would declare that the place is not lighted by the sun without, but that the rays are produced within itself."

A book could be written solely on Santa Sophia's mosaics. Their beauty and splendor influenced much of this art form as seen elsewhere in the world. They are intricately woven into the history of religion and the various periods when images were and were not tolerated within a place of worship. Many of the early mosaics were destroyed or removed during the so-called Iconoclast period or Anti-Image Ban. Many superior ones date from the period after the lifting of that ban in 843.

A great many mosaics were covered over with plaster after Santa Sophia became a mosque under the Turks in 1453. Since 1932, these have been uncovered and restored, thanks to the work of the Byzantine Institute of America, the cooperation of the former Turkish ruler, Kemal Ataturk, and of the present Turkish government.

## INFLUENCES OF SANTA SOPHIA

Writers and artists were not the only ones influenced by the Church of Santa Sophia. One historian tells how the great beauty of Santa Sophia determined the adoption of the Christian religion by Russia in the tenth century. Previously, various pagan forms of religion had been practiced in that country. Prince Vladimir, however, thoroughly exploring the Mohammedan, Roman, Greek and

Hebrew religions, sent out investigators far and wide to observe "by whom and how God was worshiped." The emissaries sent to Constantinople were so overwhelmed by the beauty of the Church of Santa Sophia and the worship of God in the Orthodox ritual, that Vladimir decreed in 989 that Russia's religion should henceforth be that of the Orthodox Church.

In 1054 occurred "The Great Schism." This was a definite split between Byzantine and Roman Christianity, influenced more by political disagreements between the Byzantine and Roman regimes than by the slight differences in their beliefs. The Church of Santa Sophia was the scene of bitter disputes, and in the end the rift between the Roman Catholic and the Byzantine or Orthodox Churches was complete.

In 1204 the Crusaders of the Fourth Crusade, though supposedly bound for the Holy Land, invaded Constantinople setting fire to large sections of the city and massacring thousands of followers of the Orthodox Church. More eager for booty than for religion, they stormed the Church of Santa Sophia, stole many costly decorations, destroyed the magnificent pulpit, and tore the great gold and silver altar to bits. Later, some amends were made by the Crusaders, but they did not restore the church to its original splendor.

Nearly 250 years later came the final fall of Constantinople. This time the attackers were the fanatical forces of the Turks under the conquering Sultan Mohammad II. Constantine Paleologus, also known as Constantine XII, was the ruler in Constantinople. His forces and defense had been weakened by religious conflict that had sown seeds of discontent, dissension, and sedition. He could muster only 8000 men against the Turkish force of some 200,000. He had appealed for aid to the Pope in Rome, but the anti-Roman animosities of many Greek Catholics destroyed what chances there might have otherwise been for such help.

In the siege, Constantine Paleologus himself was killed. On May 29, 1453, as capture of the city became certain, its inhabitants turned to Santa Sophia as a place of prayer and refuge. From all parts of the city they poured into the great church. Inside of an hour it was filled with a terrified crowd of 10,000. According to

Edward Gibbon, they included "multitudes of fathers and husbands, of women and children, of priests, monks, and religious virgins."[15]

The doors of the edifice were barred on the inside, but the Turks broke them down with axes. Encountering no resistance, they took many thousands of prisoners, and stripped the church of its treasures.

The Sultan rode in triumph to the palace of the emperors and by the following Friday was celebrating with Moslem prayers in the Church of Santa Sophia.

In one respect, the Turks proved themselves more humane than the Christian Crusaders. They did not destroy Santa Sophia's mosaics. However, following the principles of their own religion, they spread plaster over these mosaics and obliterated any symbols of the Christian faith. In fact, the new Turkish rulers ordered a thorough, skilled job of repair and restoration. Thus they helped to preserve for posterity the great church, now converted into a mosque.

Since that time, many Turkish sultans have imitated the architecture of Santa Sophia in their own building programs. During 1550–1555, an Armenian architect named Sinan built for Soliman I, known also as Suleiman the Magnificent, a splended mosque in which the influence of Santa Sophia may be traced. Then there was also the beautiful and impressive Blue Mosque, built during 1608–1614 for Sultan Ahmed, and still entrancing to visitors to modern Istanbul. Its dome is a lasting illustration of how Moslem architecture came to be based on Byzantine forms and in particular on the forms first perfected in Santa Sophia. Thus the beautiful dome of Santa Sophia became a model for a whole series of noteworthy mosques.

Over the centuries, many earthquakes damaged Santa Sophia. Between the fifth and the middle of the fifteenth centuries alone, twenty-three earthquakes have been recorded. Shocks in 1033 were reported to have continued 140 days. Many more have been recorded since. Time and again parts of the beautiful soaring dome have cracked or fallen, but repairs have always restored its beauty and proportions. In 1847, two Italian architects, the Fossati brothers, were commissioned by the Turkish sultan, Abdul Mecid, to undertake one of the greatest repairs in the church's history. The dome

was secured by a chain fastened completely around it; the structure as a whole was thoroughly overhauled, and the interior redecorated.

Santa Sophia is today a Turkish state museum rather than a mosque. This change was made during the presidency of Kemal Ataturk, who held office from 1923 to 1938 and brought about far-reaching changes, tending to westernize and modernize Turkey. The Turkish government has continued to maintain Santa Sophia as a treasured monument of art, open to all visitors. Despite the many necessary renovations and repairs, the building has undergone relatively little basic change.

In the mid-summer of 1967 Pope Paul VI traveled from Rome to Istanbul in an official visit announced as a gesture toward the re-unification of the Roman and Orthodox branches of the Catholic faith. Escorted only by the Turkish foreign minister, the Pope toured Santa Sophia and, while there, dropped for a short time to his knees to pray before the ceiling portrayal of the Virgin Mary and infant Jesus, flanked on either side by Arabic script letters meaning "Allah" and "Mohammed."

This, according to news commentators, constituted the first publicly performed Christian prayers in that structure since 1453 when it ceased to be a church. The Pope's gesture attracted particular attention because the radical pro-Moslem religious groups in Turkey want Santa Sophia to be reconverted from a museum to a mosque. Their newspapers, in fact, asserted that the real purpose behind this first papal visit was to launch a crusade "to convert all Turks to Christianity."

The significance of Santa Sophia as structure and symbol is obviously not merely a matter of the past!

# IX

## MACHU PICCHU

---

## AN INCA ENIGMA

Viracocha, Lord of the Universe . . .
Where are you?
. . . He may be above,
He may be below,
Or alight in the sky;
Where is his council seat?
Hear me!

—Ancient Inca Ritual Song

Cradled in a "saddle" formed between two high and remote peaks in the Andes, lies the fabulous Lost City of the Incas, Machu Picchu (pronounced Ma-chew Peek-chew). Abandoned and lost in almost inaccessible wilds during four hundred years, it is perched on a narrow ridge at an altitude of 6750 feet, some 2000 feet above the Urubamba River. No one can say just how old Machu Picchu is, but it is believed to have been the last residence and stronghold of the Inca rulers after the Spanish conquest in the sixteenth century.

The towering peaks on either side are called Huayna Picchu (young peak) and Machu Picchu (old peak) for which the city was named by the man who re-discovered it in 1911.

No longer is the Lost City of the Incas merely the creation of some writer's imagination. Explorers, historians, and archaeologists have now demonstrated its reality. Books, maps, photographs, and tourists can report on and describe its terraces, temples, sacred plazas, residential compounds, gabled houses, and barracks for soldiers.

Today, a railway links the area with Cuzco and a five-mile-long winding highway climbs the approach to the ancient templed citadel.

In 1911, Hiram Bingham, a young American historian, went to Peru to search for the last Inca capital, Vilcapampa. He journeyed first to Cuzco, one of the oldest and most interesting cities in the Americas, situated in the southeast part of the country, and once the Inca capital. From there his travels took him about fifty miles northwest through the valleys and mountain wilds of the Cordillera Vilcabamba.

As a historian, Bingham had acquainted himself with old records dealing with the history of the Incas. Since the Incas, like other South American peoples, had no written language, their history was a remembered one, handed down from generation to generation. Their only records were the *quipus*—the colored knotted strings, with knots so sized and positioned on the strings as to indicate messages, information, and numbered statistics, including a decimal system. These *quipus* were used in conjunction with oral communication. Today there are no readers or rememberers who can interpret these knotted records.

Written records finally were put down immediately after and in the years following the Spanish conquest under Francisco Pizarro in 1532. Spaniards, priests, and other chroniclers who had had some contact with the remaining remnants of the Inca people began to write the history of this civilization. Archaeologists and historians have added to the sum of information.

## THE DISCOVERY

Machu Picchu (whether this was Vilcapampa is still uncertain today, as the name the Incas gave it is unknown to us) was never mentioned by either the Incas or the Spaniards. The location of this favorite residence of Inca chiefs was a secret they kept well from the common people and from the Spanish conquerors seeking gold and treasures.

Bingham's search for Vilcapampa was a test of endurance and patience. In the company of two friends, one a naturalist, the other a surgeon, and a police sergeant provided by the Peruvian government to act as interpreter, he explored valleys, climbed almost inaccessible peaks, crossed perilous streams and rivers, and beat his way through dense jungles. All along the way, in villages, hamlets, and on the difficult overgrown trails, he questioned everyone he met.

One day, leaving his friends behind at their camping site, and guided only by a small boy, Bingham and the sergeant set out to find some ruins reported by Indian farmers in that remote area. Suddenly, on rounding a projection in the road, they came upon a tremendous flight of stone-faced terraces. There were about a hundred of them, each about ten feet high and hundreds of feet long. Bingham had already seen some terraces along the way and was not unduly excited.

In this case, the Indian farmers in the neighborhood had cleared much of the jungle-covered area of these ledges and were using the rich soil for growing crops.

Following their small guide across one of these terraces and into a dense forest beyond, Bingham and the sergeant suddenly glimpsed through the tangled growth of centuries the ruins of white granite houses, built in the manner of the Incas' finest stone work.

As they climbed further, new surprises awaited them. One by one, beautiful structures were revealed: a cave, lined with finely cut stone (a royal mausoleum); a semicircular building with sloping, curving sides (a temple of the sun); a wall, one of the few in Inca architecture, so perfectly built that Bingham said in the beauty of its flow and symmetry it far surpassed the best Inca walls in Cuzco, which had been the marvel of tourists for four centuries. In fact, he thought it the finest stonework in the world.

There was no mortar between the huge stones, since the Incas used none, yet they were fitted together so perfectly that they seemed to flow one into another, and a pin could not be inserted between them. Further along, Bingham, the sergeant, and their guide came to a great stairway built of huge granite masses, and two buildings each constructed of these same giant-sized white granite blocks. These structures were obviously temples and opened onto a courtyard which Bingham later named "The Sacred Plaza."

Each of these buildings had three walls, was open on one side, and was roofless. The principal temple, whose 12-foot-high walls were composed of blocks, some of which weighed from ten to fifteen tons and were higher than a man, contained beautifully fashioned niches, five on each side wall and seven on the back. Under these seven niches stood a rectangular block fourteen feet long. Bingham believed this to be either a sacrificial altar or a slab to hold the mummies of dead Inca leaders.

How did the Inca builders who did not have the advantage of the wheel, nor cranes, pulleys and winches, move and place into exact positions these massive blocks of granite? Could it have been with inclined planes and levers and the labor of countless workers? This same question has been posed for the mysterious monoliths of England's Stonehenge.

More and more wonders were revealed to Bingham that day. Close to the temple described above, stood another astounding sight. Here, the temple ruins contained three huge windows facing the rising sun and framing an awe-inspiring view of the canyon. Bingham remembered the words of a Peruvian writer of 1620 named Slacamayhua who had said that Manco the Great, the first Inca, had ordered "works to be executed at the place of his birth, consisting of a masonry wall with three windows."

This, then, could have been the city of the birth of Manco I: it could also have been the refuge and stronghold of the last of the Inca leaders. Bingham named it Machu Picchu.


## FURTHER DISCOVERIES

Bingham returned again to Machu Picchu, this time under the auspices of Yale University and the National Geographic Society. As the jungle was cut back more and more, and the ruins uncovered and cleaned, further startling discoveries were made and noted. Over the succeeding years, many archaeologists have followed in his footsteps, enriching the growing body of information about Machu Picchu.

Machu Picchu is the most distant, the largest, the most important, and most spectacular of a series of stone fortress cities laid out by the Inca builders along the top of a valley above the Urubamba gorge. These cities are about ten miles apart and are connected by a remarkable stone-laid road.

Road building and building construction were truly incredible accomplishments of the Incas. This becomes clear when we realize they not only had no mortar, nor any form of the wheel, but they also had no precision instruments, no iron or steel tools, no vehicles (except for man-carrying litters), and no horses. Their beast of burden was the llama, domesticated 2000 years earlier. Their tools were stone hammers and bronze crowbars, axes, and chisels. The Incas seem to have been the first of the peoples of the Andes to use bronze for tools.

Inca roads ran the length and breadth of the Empire, crisscrossing the country over deserts and across the tops of the Andes. There were more than ten thousand miles of highway. Like the Roman roads, to which they are only second in extent and importance, they were used principally to move armies of soldiers. Vital, also, was their use in communications. Runners, bearing the knotted *quipus,* carried their messages from place to place over these important roadways.

These couriers, traveling at high speed and sometimes at great altitudes, chewed the addictive dried coca leaves to make them less vulnerable to cold, thirst, hunger, and fatigue. Coca, from which the narcotic cocaine is derived and which the Incas called the "divine plant," is still in use today by more than five million people and especially by the Andean Indians who live and work at high altitudes.

In the city of Machu Picchu itself, streets and roads consist mostly of stone stairways, linking the buildings from bottom to top. Fifty such stairways, comprising 3000 steps, lead from the various residential quarters and plazas to the topmost temple of the three windows and the "Hitching Post of the Sun." Here, at this stone post or pillar, the *intihuatama,* priests were said to harness the glowing ball of fire in the sky in the practice of their state religion, the worship of the sun.

Close to this sacred section is the "Intellectual District," home of the Inca Lord, his family, and nobles while in residence in the city.

Machu Picchu, like most sanctuaries and defense towns, was self-sustaining. With the Inca's exceptional talent for agriculture, the numerous broad terraces grew the crops which helped feed the inhabitants.

Measurement of the space available for crops, however, has drawn the opinion from some authorities that it could not have supported more than 500 inhabitants.

Water gathered from the mountain streams was brought from an

aqueduct a mile from the city, flowed down the "Stairway of the Fountains," composed of sixteen descending fountains, and channeled via stone scoops or half pipes through the white granite city for drinking, bathing, the making of *chicha* (beer), and then, step by step, down through and onto the agricultural terraces.

Hiram Bingham has suggested that one of the reasons Machu Picchu had been abandoned may have been the shortage of water due to the drying up of the mountain streams. A mausoleum for the royal mummies, and a cemetery for the common people took care of the last needs of the inhabitants of Machu Picchu.

Various styles of architecture make up the fortress-city complex. Though most of the construction seems definitely Incan, some roughly built, pointed roof or two-story dwellings suggest a possible pre-Incan origin.

Most houses are grouped in compounds, each compound differing from the others in some way, either by a feature of its architecture, or by the manner in which its houses are arranged. One has very large niches in the wall, possibly large enough to hold a hunched-up mummy. These large niches, in turn, have three smaller niches, perhaps to receive offerings to the mummified remains of a relative. Houses in some compounds contain windows; some are distinguished by having three entrances; still others have other differences.

The houses of the common people appear roughly built, while the royal residences are constructed of well-fitted white granite ashlars, gabled and peaked. The roofs were undoubtedly made of thatched grass, held down by various so-called eye-bonders and stone pegs, some of which remain in the ruins today.

In many of the finer buildings, the lowest tiers of granite are massive, decreasing in size gradually as they reach the top. This produces an impression of great security as well as gracefulness.

Attesting to the Inca's skill in stonework in one house, adjoining the "Principal Temple," is a massive granite block stretching from the front door to the corner of the house on one side, and even beyond, to become a small part of the side wall. This huge stone forms the entire lower half of the wall at this point and contains the bottom portions of two of the room's niches. The amazing thing is that the great block of granite has thirty-two angles, all beautifully cut and fitted!

This same house, which authorities believe to have been a royal mausoleum, is one of the finest examples of Inca architecture and stonework. A long stone bench extends the full length of the house opposite the door, and was probably used as a slab on which to place the mummies of the Inca Lords. The many niches with which the walls are lined are so nearly alike in size and shape as to show scarcely any difference. Here, one should point out again that since the Incas had no precision instruments, the trained eyes of their artistic architects and builders must have been truly remarkable.

The care lavished on this magnificent structure, and the fact that a beautifully built stone stairway leads from it to the *intihuatama*, the sun-worshiping stone above, points to its obvious importance in the community.

All interiors were extremely simple. It is believed the houses contained no furniture. Only the chiefs used a stool. The ordinary Inca sat upon a floor of beaten earth or upon a pile of blankets made from the wool of the llama or alpaca. The wool of the vicuña, much prized in our modern society, served as a cloak for the Inca Lord, and was taboo for the common man. It was usually woven by one of the Chosen Women, of whom we will have more to say later, and was worn only once by the Inca chief—and then destroyed. Niches placed at various levels in the walls seem to have taken the place of furniture. Stone pegs protruding from the walls between the niches made handy hooks for various household purposes.

The tall doors, like those of ancient Egypt, are narrower at the top than the bottom. Windows and even niches in the walls seem to follow this pattern. It has been recorded that the Inca did not lock his door. Instead, when he left his home, he placed a small wooden stick across its threshold to notify all that he was absent and that no one could enter. Though the Inca had very little in the way of personal property, and was clothed and fed by the Inca Lord he served, it nevertheless speaks well for his honesty.

Various kinds of pottery have been found at Machu Picchu, some definitely Incan, others apparently non-Incan, though their origin is as yet unknown. Found also were many of the huge pointed-bottom jars used for holding *chicha,* the beer of the Inca. This was their favorite fermented beverage. It was made from sprouted corn, first boiled, then chewed by the women until their saliva converted the starch into sugar, then boiled once more.

Many bronze shawl pins found among the ruins are identical with those with which the modern Andean Indian woman fastens her shawl today.

A note in favor of modern day conservationists is Bingham's explanation for the use of stone rather than wood in construction. The absence of trees in the Peruvian highlands, he states, was not due to the altitude, since he found forests growing at more than 15,000 feet in the almost inaccessible heights of the Cordillera Vilcabamba. Rather, he points out, the need for fuel over very long periods of human habitation had decimated the forests in those areas.


THE RESIDENTS

What of the last residents of the lost city? The first searches through the ruins of Machu Picchu yielded very little trace of its former inhabitants. A further thorough probing of the caves and graves found in the surrounding area, however, uncovered enough bones to be able to determine that, of 173 people buried, 150 had been women. Since the bones of muscular people were not found in the caves, it has been deduced that only people of high rank were allowed burial in this manner, while the workers who labored to produce the food and serve the city and its inhabitants were buried elsewhere.

It is Bingham's theory, and some historians do not agree, that Machu Picchu became the sanctuary and hiding place from the Spaniards of the Chosen Women of the Sun after many of them had received cruel treatment at the hands of the conquerors.

These Chosen Women, sometimes called the Virgins of the Sun, were literally chosen for their beauty, grace, and talent. All girls in the Inca Empire above the age of ten were counted and classified.

The ones picked to be Chosen Women consecrated their lives to the service of the sun and to the Inca rulers and priests.

Under the supervision of older Chosen Women, they learned to become skilled weavers, to prepare the special foods and beverages used on state occasions, and to make the robes and hangings used by the nobles. At the age of sixteen they were divided into three classes according to their beauty. Some of the most beautiful became concubines of the Inca Emperor, or served the priests in the worship of the sun; others became sacrifices to the sun or remained for life as temple attendants and instructors of other Chosen Women; a third group served as wives given to nobles or military leaders as awards for services rendered.

## AN ABBREVIATED INCA HISTORY

The cultural traditions of the Inca Empire have been traced back to about 2500 B.C.E. Though archaeologists and historians differ as to the date of the emergence of the Inca, and accuracy seems impossible due to the lack of a written language, it is generally believed that the legendary figure of the first Inca Lord, Manco Capac, appeared about 1000 C.E., that he came from the southeast around Lake Titicaca, and founded the city of Cuzco.

Over the years that followed, the Incas, by conquering and absorbing rival and surrounding tribes, expanded their territory and influence. At one time, their empire controlled some six million people, included much of Ecuador and Chile, as well as Peru, and extended over 3000 miles.

One of the peoples conquered about 1350 C.E. gave to the Incas their official language—*Quechua*, still widely used today. It is estimated that about half of Peru's inhabitants now speak it. It is not known what language was spoken before *Quechua* was adopted.

The word, *Quechua*, means "warm-valley-people," and it is believed that this is also the name the Incas gave to themselves. "Inca" was the word they used for their Lords or Emperors, but the Spaniards applied it to all the native ruling class. Today, we use the term, Inca, to cover the entire race.

Aside from their traditional skills as great agriculturists and engineers, they were efficient organizers and administrators. Though they expanded and grew by means of fighting and absorption, they did not glorify war. Rather, they seemed to have had a strong ethical foundation. One writer has likened the Inca system to that of "a welfare state of a particularly despotic kind." They had no money, goods being exchanged for services. Their social unit was the *ayulla*, a communal sharing of land, animals, and crops by groups, or clans.

After about 1438, and their defeat of the Chancas, a particularly aggressive neighboring tribe, the Incas expanded their rule rapidly, adding to their territory and population. Under the Inca Pachacuti, who lived during this period and has been considered one of the greatest of the Inca rulers, the empire contained about 155,000 square miles of territory. Some writers credit the building of Machu Picchu to Pachacuti during this great period of expansion. It is their contention that Pachacuti waged war against hostile savage tribes in that area and built the fortress city on the heights above the humid jungles in an attempt to dominate the area. Hiram Bingham, however, does not believe the beautiful granite temples of Machu Picchu were built as a fortress city, though its location made it practically immune from attack. It was under Topa Inca, who succeeded Pachacuti in 1471, that the great road-building program was begun.

The Inca Empire continued to expand, but in the sixteenth century it was beset by a long series of civil wars. Weakened by this inner turmoil and dissension, it was easily conquered for Spain by Francisco Pizarro and a mere handful of 130 foot soldiers, bearing their mystifying and formidable firearms.

In November of 1532, the thirteenth Inca Lord, Atahualp a, was captured by Pizarro at Cajamarca, and held for ransom by the treasure-hungry conquerors. Though enormous amounts of gold and silver were paid to the Spaniards as ransom, they nevertheless slew Atahualpa. The ransom, plus the treasure of the ransacked country, containing some of the finest statuary by Peru's best goldsmiths, under an edict of the Spanish Emperor Charles V, dated February 13, 1535, were "melted in the royal mints at Sevilla, Toledo and Segovia."

Gold was also valued by the Incas. They had accumulated vast stores of it, thought of it as divine, and called it "the teardrops of the sun."

By 1535, the Empire of the Incas had been brought completely under control of the Spanish conquerors.

Manco II, grandson of the famous Emperor Huyana the Great, was crowned as a puppet Inca chief by the Spaniards. However, in 1537, he rebelled, led a revolt against them, and fled from Cuzco with a large force to the natural fortress of the Urubamba Valley and Vilcapampa, which some historians believed to be identical with the sanctuary of Machu Picchu. Here, Manco established a Neo-Inca state, and from this impregnable height led many raids upon the Spaniards. The Inca weapons, bolas and slings, competed with the blunderbusses of the invaders.

Attempts of Pizarro and of his brother Gonzalo Pizarro, to rout out Manco II and his men, failed. It was impossible to use horses in these wilds, and the expeditions on foot proved so exhausting in these heights, that the Spaniards were easily ambushed and killed.

Lookout posts atop the mountains where signal fires could be lit gave ample warning and preparation to Manco and his men. The remains of two such signal towers have been found near Machu Picchu, one atop Huayna Picchu, and the other on the crest of the mountain of Machu Picchu itself.

Civil war and disputes between the Spanish conquerors finally brought about the assassination of Francisco Pizarro in 1541.

For thirty-five years, between 1537 and 1572, the surviving Inca Lords and their followers, waged guerrilla warfare against the Spaniards out of the sanctuary of Vilcapampa.

In 1571, Tupac Amaru, third son of Manco II, ruled at Vilcapampa. He had been brought up by the Chosen Women of the Sun and was married to one of them. Kept in seclusion most of his life by his jealous brother, the Inca Lord Titu Cusi, now dead, he had been untrained in the ways of ruling or soldiering.

Meanwhile, Philip II of Spain, through his Viceroy, Don Francisco de Toledo, was determined to bring the Indians of the Vilcapampa area into submission. An ambassador, sent to lure the young Inca Lord to Cuzco, was waylaid by Inca warriors and killed.

When this was followed by news of the murder of a Spanish priest, the Viceroy vowed to exterminate the royal Inca family.

One day, a Spanish expedition, well provided with arms, ammunition, and promises of monetary rewards for success, overtook Tupac Amaru in the jungles where the inexperienced young ruler had fled from his sanctuary. He was brought in triumph to Cuzco, and there, in 1572, he, his wife and family, and the remaining Inca chiefs were brutally tortured and put to death. The Inca Empire was at an end.

In 1780–1781, there was an abortive attempt of the Andean Indians to rebel against Spanish rule. Their leader, José Gabriel Condorcanqui, who called himself Tupac Amaru II, was defeated and executed. The Inca story was over.

Though the history of the Inca has come to an end, research into its civilization goes on. Modern archaeology with the latest methods of scientific excavation, its aerial and stratigraphical techniques, and the use of Carbon-14 tests in determining age, is uncovering additional information. Perhaps, one day Machu Picchu will yield new answers to its mysteries.

That remarkably beautiful city, with its imposing awe-inspiring location between the two towering precipices, may well have been the home and sanctuary of the last Inca rulers and the refuge of the Chosen Women of the Sun, as suggested by Hiram Bingham. Perhaps, they died here, one by one, leaving no descendants and no written records to answer all the many questions that still are asked today.

In 1967, however, discovery of the "real" Vilcapampa at a different site was claimed by another American, Gene Savoy. In the company of a Peruvian explorer, Savoy set out to refute the theory that Machu Picchu was identical with Vilcapampa. After months of exploration the expedition brought them to the "Plain of the Spirits" where they found ancient Inca ruins covered over by dense jungle and great trees. A luxurious palace, various complexes of limestone and granite houses, fountains, terraces, and courtyards, led them to the conclusion that there indeed lay the lost Inca capital, Vilcapampa. Savoy says that Bingham himself actually had reached

these same ruins without knowing it, but was frightened off by
hostile Indians living in the area.

So the Lost City of the Incas remains a fascinating riddle still.
But what we do know for certain is that Hiram Bingham—later a
governor and senator of the State of Connecticut—did discover and
open up for the world, the awesomely beautiful ancient Inca city
on the heights known now as Machu Picchu, a magnet that draws
increasing thousands of today's travelers.

# X

## THE TAJ MAHAL

---

## THE TOMB LIKE A JEWEL

When in our hurried time we see enormous structures
of a hundred stories raised in a year or two, and then consider
how twenty-two thousand men toiled for twenty-two years
on this little tomb . . .
we begin to sense the difference between industry and art.

—WILL DURANT, *Our Oriental Heritage*

Over 300 years ago in India, one of the Mogul rulers built for his wife a tomb which many artists and architects have called the most beautiful and perfect of all buildings on earth. Certainly the Taj Mahal is the most exquisite mausoleum in the world.

In it, side by side, lie the remains of Shah Jahan and his wife, Mumtaz Mahal, whose name means "Ornament of the Palace." Shah Jahan built the tomb in memory of his love and as a tribute to her fertility. Its name, "Taj Mahal," means "Crown of the Palace" another of the titles given to Mumtaz.

Mumtaz Mahal was Shah Jahan's favorite wife. He married her when he was twenty-one, and adored this new spouse. Their great love has been told and retold by writers and historians. Mumtaz Mahal was a wise and generous woman who frequently advised her husband. In 1630 she died in childbirth at the age of thirty-nine. She had given birth to fourteen children in eighteen years. Her husband was grief stricken and vowed to build his wife a tomb lovelier than any on earth. A year after her death, work was begun on the mausoleum.

The exquisite structure that results, and the tender sentiment that it expresses, might lead us to assume that Shah Jahan was a gentle, peaceful soul. The records of history, however, present a far different picture.

The Taj Mahal, supreme specimen of Moslem architecture and construction, stands at Agra, about 125 miles from Delhi, once the capital of India. To Delhi in 1526 came as conqueror Shah Jahan's ancestor Babur (or Baber) a descendant of the great Tamerlane (or Timur Lang) who had established his rule in northern Afghanistan in the last part of the fourteenth century.

Babur is commonly called India's first Mogul ruler. Mogul—also spelled sometimes Moghul, Moghal, or Mughal—is in reality the Persian or Arabic form of the name *Mongol*. However, Mongolia, land of the Mongols, is distant from both Afghanistan and India.

The connection must be traced in terms of great tribal migrations and expeditions of conquest. They carried the bearers of the Mongol name across the heart of Asia, far toward the west and south. These great marches can be traced back to, and even beyond, the days of the mighty Mongol emperor, Genghis (or Jenghiz) Khan (1162–1227 C.E.)

We cannot ascertain today that Genghis Khan, Tamerlane, Babur, and his descendants, the Great Mogul emperors of India, were all in one direct line of descent. Yet they are linked, if not by direct family ties, then by the twisting and turnings of names that are so common in history.

The name Mogul came to be applied to almost all Mohammedan peoples from the countries lying to the west and northwest of India, even though their ancestors had not always come from Mongolia itself!

The title "Great Mogul" was commonly given to the ruling emperor of the dynasty founded by Babur—a dynasty that endured during more than 300 years. Even today, the word "mogul" in a popular sense has come to mean a particularly powerful, imposing, or influential person.

Part of the legendary pomp of Babur, founder of the dynasty, came from the fact that the great Koh-i-nur diamond was included in the rich booty that he gained in his conquest of India.

Among the Great Moguls who followed Babur, the personality most appealing to modern readers of history was the ruler called Akbar the Great, Emperor of Hindustan (1542–1605). He ruled during the period of Elizabeth I in England, Philip II in Spain, and Ivan the Terrible in Russia.

Akbar was notably tolerant for his era in regard to religion. He gained an enviable reputation for sound sense and moderation. He has been called the justest and wisest of all Asian rulers. Akbar's wife, a Hindu princess, bore a son, Jehangir, who took the throne after Akbar died.

Jehangir appears to have been a cruel and degenerate personality. Some chroniclers believe even that the death of Akbar was not natural, but rather that he was poisoned by his son, Jehangir, or by Jehangir's orders. Whether or not outright murder placed Jehangir on the throne, his power was established amid intrigue, treachery, and cruelties.

His reign ended similarly. Shah Jahan, son of Jehangir, seized the throne, ruthlessly eliminating the claims of his brothers. Like his father, Shah Jahan began as a cruel, extravagant, and licentious ruler. Industry and commerce suffered under the burdens of his heavy court costs and the high salaries with which he rewarded his courtiers and officials.

In spite of his enormous outlays, Shah Jahan managed to keep his coffers full. He was reported to have two underground treasuries, each with 150,000 cubic feet capacity, filled with gold and silver.

In religious matters too, Shah Jahan was a tyrant. His grandfather Akbar had been notably tolerant. His father Jehangir had not cared much, one way or another, about religion. Shah Jahan, however, tried to force all his subjects into the Moslem faith. He persecuted Christians, destroyed many Hindu shrines, and in the very year that he began to build his Taj Mahal, he decreed a halt to the construction of Hindu temples and places of worship.

In fairness, some of the more favorable qualities of Shah Jahan should be mentioned also. Toward his friends he was generous; toward the poor in his realm he could be at times a protector and helper; and toward his wife, Mumtaz Mahal, while she lived and after, he displayed a devotion that has become proverbial. This intolerant, greedy, tyrannical, and paradoxical ruler had a passion for stunningly beautiful architecture. He indulged his artistic tastes by pouring out half of his huge revenues for the promotion of architecture and other arts. The Taj Mahal was only one among a hundred masterpieces that Shah Jahan is credited with having built. India never before had witnessed such a surge of new beauty in its buildings.

Shah Jahan, too, fell victim to cruelty and filial treachery. One of his sons, Aurangzeb, deposed him and made him a prisoner. For nine

years, until he died in 1666, he was held captive in the Fort of Agra. Here, alone, embittered and neglected, he was attended only by his faithful daughter, Johanara. From the Jasmine Tower of his prison, Shah Jahan could look across the Jumna River to the Taj Mahal, the jeweled tomb he had built for his beloved Empress.

Aurangzeb was an intolerant religious fanatic. He went much further than his father and destroyed hundreds of Hindu temples which had housed the art of India for a thousand years. Within 17 years after Aurangzeb's death, the empire of India, built into a great civilization by joint efforts of Hindus and Moslems, was diminished in territory and broken in power.

## OUTSIDE INFLUENCES IN INDIAN ART

H. G. Wells, in tracing the course of art in India, has pointed out that its various conquerors have brought with them the germs of highly developed architecture. To these, however, India added her own delicate refinements and elaborations.

Stone architecture became prevalent in India only after the Greek invasion. Buddhist art, dating from the first four centuries c.e., also shows the Hellenic influence.

Not until the fifth and sixth centuries c.e., under the Gupta dynasty, did Indian architecture and sculpture attain a style and quality of its own.

The Moslem conquest of India brought to that country the chief forms of the Islamic style: the minaret, and the pointed arch. The bulbous inverted onion-shape dome was definitely Persian. To these were added jewel-like finishes, delicate carvings, exquisite window tracery, and intricately pierced screens.

The Taj Mahal, most splendid specimen of Moslem architecture, became a harmonious fusion of influences from within and from outside India. The Indian influences have often been overlooked, especially since three foreigners are usually given credit for the architecture—Ustad Isa, a Persian; Gieronimo Veronee, an Italian; and Austin de Bordeaux, a Frenchman.

Careful students of Indian art now stress that the Taj Mahal was strongly influenced by the first true Mogul monument, the tomb of Humayun in Delhi, built by his widow, Haji Begam. It had struck a new and impressive note, with its eight-sided form, its parklike setting, and its free, open, and magnificent effects. This influential building still stands at Delhi. It is not comparable in exquisite grace to the Taj Mahal, but the latter could hardly have become what it is without the example and inspiration of this earlier masterpiece.

Charles Fabri compares the Humayun tomb to "the earth" but the Taj Mahal to "a cloud in a dream."[16] The former was built for a warrior and strong man, the latter for "a slender little woman, gentle, sweet, and yielding." Hence it is fitting that one should be "a masculine structure," and the other should seem "feminine."

The skilled artisans who completed the Taj Mahal were brought from Moslem centers as distant as Baghdad and Constantinople. No part in design or fabrication appears to have been given to Hindus, however.

Reports vary as to the time required to complete the Taj Mahal. Almost certainly it took between seventeen and twenty-two years. Probably some 22,000 men worked on it. The village of Tan Gaj, built to house the workers, still stands.

Though the Maharajah of Jaipur presented the marble as a gift to Shah Jahan, the cost of the tomb was enormous, even for those days of royal splendor and extravagance.


THE GARDENS

Engraved over the tall entrance gate in the high crenellated red sandstone wall surrounding the tomb and its gardens, is an old Arabic text: "No one shall enter the garden of God unless he is pure of heart."

Almost all Moslem tombs are enclosed by gardens. Their design, influenced by Persian culture, reached its heights in India under the Moguls. The spacious gardens of the Taj Mahal with their subtle combinations of sun and shade, water, flowers, trees, and fruit, have remained a lovely and fitting example of great landscape architecture.

When one looks across the graceful gardens and down the long slender pool framed in thick masses of dark yew and cypress trees, the tomb itself seems like an apparition out of an old fairy tale.

Its inverted white reflections in the dark pool stimulates the imagination, adding further to the feeling of unreality.

Behind the sentinel-like trees lie thick and massive bushes, and beyond these stretch sweeps of green lawn with clumps of fragrant red, purple, blue, and gold flowers. Humming bees and countless gay butterflies hover over the spectacularly colorful blooms, and the garden also abounds in brilliant parrots and birds of all descriptions. Occasionally, white storks fly across the blue sky, adding to the delight of the scene.

## THE TOMB

As one nears the gleaming white marble mosque and its delicate details begin to reveal themselves, one becomes increasingly aware of its utter perfection.

This is a perfection having nothing to do with size. Will Durant, in his book *Our Oriental Heritage,* remarks:

> "When in our hurried time we see enormous structures of a hundred stories raised in a year or two, and then consider how twenty-two thousand men toiled for twenty-two years on this little tomb, hardly a hundred feet high, we begin to sense the difference between industry and art."[17]

The great domed Taj Mahal rises from a black-and-white-checked marble terrace at the end of the oblong tree-lined pool. This terraced platform, a square of about 315 feet on edge, is built upon a red sandstone base. Growing out of the corners of the building are the handsome smaller-domed mosques. At each corner, but standing apart from the structure, are four graceful minarets.

These slender minarets, 130 feet tall, are of white marble, and have three stories, each with balconies. The whole is topped by an open lantern surmounted by a bulbous dome with a spire.

Minaret is the Arabic word for lighthouse. Minarets are native to Mohammedan architecture, and are derived originally from the great lighthouse of Alexandria called the Pharos. Here in the seventh century, the Moslem conquerors placed a small chamber for prayers in its top story. The lighthouse motive has remained today in all the myriads of minarets that rise beside mosques.

All exterior surfaces of the Taj Mahal are formed from large expanses of polished white marble on which flowers of onyx and turquoise are delicately carved. Jewel-like incrustations sparkle and gleam.

Religious texts and hieroglyphs inlaid with black marble stand out strikingly. Every portico of white marble seems aglow with precious metals and costly stones.

Even the spandrels, that portion between the arches as well as the spaces between the tops of the arches and the roof or windows above, are inlaid with gemlike stones. Agates, bloodstones, carnelians, lapis lazuli, jaspers, and other semi-precious stones are combined in wreaths, scrolls, and frets, exquisitely designed and magnificent in color, enhanced by the pure white marble of their background.

At one time, the main entrance consisted of two massive silver doors, but these were carried off by plunderers in 1796.

The interior is relatively simple. The impressive curving dome overhead with a diameter of nearly sixty feet, rises to a height of eighty feet over the building's roof. Beneath this central dome in the echoing chamber, lie the two small sarcophagi of Shah Jahan and Mumtaz Mahal. At one time a golden railing encrusted with semiprecious stones enclosed this area. However, over the years, thieves have robbed the tomb of this abundance of jewels.

Aurangzeb, Shah Jahan's son, had the golden railing replaced. Instead, we see an octagonal screen of almost transparent marble so finely carved as to resemble delicate lace. It is formed from a single block of marble and reaches the height of a man.

The marble screen of the Taj Mahal is unsurpassed in beauty, even by the famous screen and halo of bronze that accompanies the great sculpture of the Buddha seated in a lotus bud at Horiuji in Japan.

The coffinlike tomb of Mumtaz Mahal lies on an elevation in the center of the enclosed area formed by the screen. Her husband's sepulcher, a much larger construction, lies a little to one side. It was placed there by his son, Aurangzeb.

Shah Jahan's original plans for his own interment were for a black mausoleum to be erected the other side of the Jumna River and linked by a bridge to the tomb of his beloved wife. Aurangzeb arranged otherwise. Actually, the bodies of both husband and wife were buried in a crypt below these tombs.

Mumtaz Mahal's tomb is skillfully encrusted with precious stones, which are artfully so arranged as to make it difficult to tell where one has been joined to another. One jeweled flower alone, scarcely an inch square, contains sixty different inlays. In a single carnation leaf can be found thirty-five different kinds of carnelian.

The corner rooms under the smaller domes of the mausoleum are about thirty feet in diameter. From these corner rooms, marble screens filter the light into the main area, adding to the fascinating play of light and shade and the glow of colorful stones against white marble.

From each tiny exquisite detail to the over-all long view, the Taj Mahal is a thing of beauty.

Framing the mausoleum to create a perfect picture when seen from afar, are two simple red sandstone mosques, one at each end. These best complement the whole setting, when it is viewed from the nearby river Jumna.

Some say the most magical time to see the Taj Mahal is in moonlight; others say the dawn. But at any time of the day, the mausoleum is exquisitely lovely.

# XI

## THE PANAMA CANAL

---

## CUT BETWEEN TWO CONTINENTS

Fix limits to the wild waves' race,
And bind the seas with firm embrace.

— J. W. GOETHE, *Faust*, PART II
translation by John Anster

S tories of great structures seem likely to lead, sooner or later, to the use of superlatives—words that mean the most of some quality, such as oldest, longest, tallest, bulkiest, and biggest. One learns to be careful about these terms and to try to look behind them for the real human significance of the works to which they are applied.

Many a book and article published during the past fifty or sixty years has described the Panama Canal as the greatest engineering achievement in history. Whether one comes to consider it the greatest or only one of the greatest, it assuredly represents a mighty victory over obstacles of many kinds, and a landmark in the progress of man's mastery over a hostile nature.

Certainly the Panama Canal overshadowed any single, integrated project that modern, machine-using construction methods had completed by the time it began to operate in August, 1914. And during all the years since 1914 this aquatic "short cut" between the Atlantic and Pacific Oceans has eliminated travel distance, time, and costs for immense amounts of important shipping.

Today, intercoastal vessels, such as those bound from New York to San Francisco harbors, pass through the fifty-mile canal in as little as six to eight hours in all, at an average cost of about $5000 in canal fees. In this way they are spared more than 7800 miles of additional voyaging by sea, around the difficult southern tip of South America, known as Cape Horn.

Such a roundabout voyage would require about twenty days at sea, even with today's freight vessels, and its added cost in fuel and pay to crew and officers would come to about fifty thousand dollars!

Thus the difficult cut between two continents—also known famil-iarly as "the Big Ditch"—is an active asset in international and intercoastal transportation and trade.

This canal became a reality only after a long series of events marked by conflicts, setbacks, and often confusion.

The urge to find, or form, a safe and relatively rapid route from Europe to the Far East strengthened in the late fifteenth century. It was fed by the fact that the Turks in capturing Constantinople, the long-time capital of the Eastern or Byzantine Empire, now domi-nated the former trade routes to India and the Far East.

Columbus was seeking such a hoped-for "westward passage to Cathay" when, instead, he encountered islands near North America. As the land masses were explored and charted, a disappointing truth became all too clear: North America and South America were joined by the land link we call Central America. Together they formed a vast barrier across the westward route to Cathay, another name for China!

Even that slender link or isthmus, at its narrowest, was an impas-sable obstacle to sailing vessels. There was no gap in it.

Now, Spanish and Portuguese began their merciless plundering of great sections of this New World. Other rising powers of Europe moved in, also, to grab their share, or the share of some weaker nation. The seizure of treasure, resources, and native populations in North and South America did not, however, answer the hopes for some passage by water to the Pacific Ocean, and on to Cathay.

In the mid-sixteenth century, Antonio Galvaa, one of the great navigators of Portugal, declared in a printed work that such a passage could be created by means of a man-made canal. He named four possible routes across the isthmus of Central America. From south to north, they may be identified as (1) Darien, (2) Panama, (3) Nicaragua, and (4) Tehuantepec.

The first two of these suggested routes lie within the present boundaries of the Republic of Panama. The third is near the southern boundary of Nicaragua. The fourth, and northernmost, is at the narrowest part of southern Mexico.

To the court of King Philip II of Spain came in 1551 a memorandum prepared by a scholar, E. L. de Gomara, in support of a canal project to be launched as soon as possible. The King of Spain, however, remained deaf to such designs. The view of the Spanish crown was that a canal, even if it could be built despite the huge obstacles of climate and geography, might become a help to the active enemies of Spain. It might assist them to get through more easily to territories that Spain controlled in the Pacific Ocean.

Even Scripture was cited by the King of Spain in rejecting a canal proposal. Referring to the contiguous continents of North and South America he said, "What God hath joined together, let no man put asunder."

Yet by 1771 the government of Spain went so far as to authorize a study of the requirements for building a canal over the Tehuante-pec route. A little later, before 1780, the Nicaragua route was also studied. Further studies looking toward canal possibilities were conducted early in the nineteenth century by the eminent German traveler and naturalist, Alexander von Humboldt. Nevertheless, no positive actions resulted.

During the 1820s the Central American countries attained independence from Spain. Then in 1848 came the electrifying announcement from California—*Gold discovered!* At Sutter's Mill! Gold was everywhere, just for the taking. . . .

The following wild rush of fortune-hunters to the Pacific Coast revived interest in canal proposals. A clumsy and costly sequence of travel was forced on thousands. They sailed by water to Panama, disembarked, crossed that tropical isthmus on land, and embarked on another vessel that then made the Pacific voyage to San Francisco.

Within a few years, the tensions between the states, and then the Civil War itself, interfered with interests that might otherwise have been turned toward canal-building by the United States.

FRENCH CANAL PROJECTS

France had for some time been a center of ideas, initiatives, and experiments in canal construction. As early as 1781 had come the completion of that nation's great Languedoc Canal. It ran between the Bay of Biscay, on France's southernmost Atlantic coast, and the Mediterranean Sea.

This "Canal du Midi," nearly 150 miles long, was not built on a level. Its designer, Paul Riquet de Bonrepos, had boldly faced the problem of taking full-sized vessels uphill and down again, while they remained always afloat in water.

The Languedoc Canal actually took ships over hills 600 feet higher than its two ends, which were at sea level. This was accomplished by means of a system of more than 100 locks, supplemented by some fifty aqueducts.

A canal lock is a kind of hydraulic elevator for raising or lowering the water level and hence vessels afloat on that water. The segments of canal between locks can thus be kept level and free from troublesome water currents. All the lifting or lowering takes place under controlled conditions within the locks.

Great gates are placed at both ends of a lock. A gate is swung open when the water level within the lock reaches the level of the water beyond the gate, in the canal channel itself.

The water level in the channel outside one end of the lock may differ substantially from that in the channel outside the other end. Thus, by adding or taking away water within the lock, the vessels within are raised or lowered from one outside level to the other. A series of locks operates like steps. To raise a vessel by a total of 600 feet, fifty locks, each with a lift of twelve feet, would suffice.

Engineer Riquet thus showed the world how ships could be made to "climb stairs" or to descend them, all in safety though not without some delay. The Languedoc Canal really added the modern concept of the lock to the tools of canal builders.

Even in simple single-level canals, locks are commonly used at entrance and exit in order to compensate for the fluctuating levels caused by tides, or by variations in the water depth in rivers.

Only one major canal connects two seas whose tidal changes are so small that it requires no locks or other hydraulic supplements. This is the famous Suez Canal, connecting the Mediterranean with the Gulf of Suez and with the Red Sea.

The concept of such a man-made channel as the Suez Canal

is very old. Some rather scanty evidence indicates that as long ago as 600 B.C.E. small vessels were being rowed or towed along an artificial waterway over this same route. It may have remained in operation till as late as 700 or 800 C.E. but finally became neglected, filled in, and thus vanished.

When Napoleon Bonaparte led the French armies into Egypt at the end of the eighteenth century, he expressed interest in the possibilities of such a canal. An engineer by the name of Leper prepared a report for him on this subject. However, it led to no direct results.

The idea, nevertheless, was nursed in the active mind of Ferdinand de Lesseps, who served as a consular representative in Egypt. Thanks to his personal friendship with the viceroy of Egypt, de Lesseps secured permission in the middle of the nineteenth century to build such a canal on a ninety-nine-year lease. A large financial advance was included in the arrangement.

The British government was not happy to find a Frenchman heading so strategic a project. However, de Lesseps' company sold shares of its stock in Egypt and in France to construct the canal which, it was agreed, would be operated under international regulation rather than run by any single nation.

Work on the canal actually started in 1854, and fifteen years later the first ship traffic traveled through the completed canal's length of slightly over 100 miles. The new channel itself was more than twenty-five feet deep. It was over seventy feet wide at the bottom, and the slope of its sides made it wider still at the surface.

Actual construction costs came to a total equivalent to about fifty-five to sixty million dollars.

Existence of the Suez Canal altered economic and political factors in Europe. It diminished by more than 3700 miles the sea distance from Western Europe to India. It saved as much as thirty-six days from the schedules of ships then plying those routes.

The leaders of imperial Britain were especially concerned by these factors. In 1875, the British government, under Prime Minister Benjamin Disraeli, bought from Egyptian stockholders nearly 177,000 shares of the stock of the Suez Canal company. The world watched while this new water highway thus came under British control, and the feared French combination was excluded.


## FRENCH EFFORTS IN PANAMA

De Lesseps, the man who had conceived and created the Suez Canal, was encouraged to seek new watery worlds to conquer. Obviously, by this time, an Atlantic-Pacific canal across the Central American isthmus was needed more acutely than ever before, since international trade and transport were rapidly expanding.

This realization was reflected to some extent in the United States. Within half a dozen years after the Suez Canal went into operation, President Ulysses S. Grant appointed a commission to investigate canal possibilities at the isthmus. The resulting report made in 1876 favored the Nicaraguan route. A company was formed, permission was secured from Nicaragua, and some excavation was done along this route.

It failed before long for it had received no funds from the U.S. government. Interests in this country were not yet sufficiently organized and determined to push through so ambitious a public project.

Once again the scene shifted across the Atlantic. In 1879 an international group was called together in Paris. The participants considered a proposal from de Lesseps for a sea-level canal across Panama. His figures indicated then that such a canal could be completed within about eight years of work.

He estimated further that by excavating about 157 million cubic yards of material, such a canal could be given a clear channel between twenty-nine and thirty feet deep and seventy-two feet wide at the bottom.

De Lesseps' prestige was high due to his Suez success. Investors were willing to put their money into this exciting new Panama project. By the end of 1880 a company had been formed. It secured the necessary permission from the government of Colombia, of which Panama was a federated state. Actual excavation was started in 1882.

## THE FIRST FAILURE

What followed was a misfortune, or even a tragedy, of miscalculations and mistakes. It developed, all too late, that the preliminary surveys had been incomplete, the planning inadequate. Sanitation and living conditions were terrible on the job in Panama. Yellow fever and malaria were spread by mosquitoes. Great numbers of workers sickened and many died. Those still able to work turned to drink to get them through the nightmarish existence. Morale and efficiency sank, and the work lagged behind schedule.

Financial controls were also ineffective. Funds were foolishly or even dishonestly spent for private purposes that did not serve the great earth-moving operations. Financial castatrophe was inevitable. Before the eight-year period had ended, the company was declared bankrupt. A French court appointed a supervisor who tried to reorganize it and to retain the valuable concession granted by Colombia.

By late 1894 a new company was launched. Construction plans were changed also. Now a lock-type, multilevel canal was to be built, rather than a sea-level channel. Work in this direction continued on a reduced scale during the period 1895 to 1899.


## NEW DECISIONS IN WASHINGTON

By this time powerful interests had influenced leading policy-makers in Washington. Their desire became increasingly clear: a modern Atlantic-Pacific canal, under sole control of the United States, rather than under a French or an international group.

United States foreign policy had become increasingly ambitious, confident, and aggressive during the closing years of the nineteenth century. In the spring of 1898, came declaration of war against Spain, by this time the most decayed and feeble imperial power in Europe.

Events followed swiftly. First the American Navy battered the warships of Spain in the bay of Manila, capital of the Philippine Islands across the Pacific. This was followed by the destruction of the entire Spanish fleet in the Caribbean Sea, off Santiago de Cuba.

By mid-August, 1898, Spain gave up. She lost Cuba, Puerto Rico, and the Philippines. All passed into the control or actual ownership of the United States.

During this brief war, millions of Americans devoured newspaper accounts of the dramatic dash of the U.S. battleship *Oregon* from the Pacific into the Caribbean theater of action. It had to voyage all the way around Cape Horn. Though it set a record en route, the conclusion was clear: a canal would have cut the elapsed time to a fraction!

Now, one after another, obstacles were swept away that had prevented previous governments in Washington from creating a United States-controlled canal across Central America.

By 1901, Britain and the U.S. discarded an agreement in force since 1850. It had pledged both powers not to seek sole control over such a canal, and had promised instead to aid private financiers who would seek to construct such a channel "for the benefit of mankind."

In 1902, the U.S. Congress approved a plan to pay up to forty million dollars for the claims and efforts of the French canal company, much of whose stock was by this time owned by American speculators with insight into the way things were moving.

Congress also authorized the U.S. to purchase from Colombia a strip of territory that could include a Panama Canal, yet to be completed. President Theodore Roosevelt quickly prepared a treaty for such a transfer of Colombian territory for ten million dollars down plus an annual rental rate.

The Senate of Colombia refused to approve this treaty, and held out for more favorable terms. It seemed, for a brief time, that the canal might be built elsewhere. Congress had provided that if the Panama strip could not be secured, then the U.S. should instead select the Nicaraguan canal route. It had been the recommended choice of experts in two commissions that reported to the federal government.

President Theodore Roosevelt, however, resorted to direct rather than diplomatic action. With encouragement given by his spokesmen, plus the protective presence of American warships offshore, a small group in the state of Panama staged a quick rebellion against Colombia. They proclaimed a new and independent Republic of Panama early in November, 1903. The U.S. government lost no time in signing a treaty with this convenient new sister-republic.

In this treaty, the U.S. was pledged to protect the independence of Panama, and Panama granted to the U.S. a canal zone strip from sea to sea ten miles wide in return for a down payment and a deferred annual rental.

Between early 1904 and the latter part of 1914 the present Panama Canal was planned, excavated, constructed, and put into actual operation by the United States. A crowded sequence of preparations, investigations, decisions, and operations were squeezed into that time.

The scope of these operations had to be tremendous—that was obvious from the start. Unexpected obstacles and setbacks, however, made the task far larger than could have been anticipated.


## A HEROIC CAMPAIGN FOR HEALTH

Before large-scale American operations could begin, the Canal Zone had to be made safe for the health of the people who had to work and live there. First of all, filth and disease needed to be conquered, no matter what kind of canal was to be built. Too many thousands of men had died already in the previous costly attempts.

Between 1904 and 1907 a great campaign was mounted to clean up the Canal Zone. Its outcome was victory—even a kind of medical triumph. Yellow fever and malaria were reduced, mainly by blocking the breeding of the disease-carrying mosquitoes.

Simple oil cans were the unsecret weapons that helped to win this battle of the war. These cans were placed at the sources of streams where they would slowly drip oil that spread in a thin film over the surface of the water. When the tiny mosquito larvae emerged from their underwater eggs, they would wriggle to the surface seeking air to breathe. The frail film of oil denied them this air. They suffocated before they could develop to maturity.

These and other measures to keep the mosquitoes from infecting human bloodstreams were applications of the pioneer discoveries of Dr. Walter Reed and his co-workers. At great personal risk, these heroes—and martyrs—of medicine had proved that yellow fever was always mosquito-borne.

The carefully planned public health campaign in the Canal Zone was under the direction of Colonel William C. Gorgas. The forces under him worked so effectively that the major health hazards had been controlled by the time heavy excavation began in 1908. By the time the canal was completed some six years later, it was said that the once-prevalent mosquitoes had become rarities in the zone.

Doctors, nurses, hospitals, and modern medical facilities, however, were no longer rarities there. Basic sanitation, sewage disposal, safe water supply, and paving appeared at the two terminal towns: Colón at the Caribbean entrance, and Panama City at the Pacific end.

Some observers might even say that the greatest building task accomplished in connection with the canal was building a complete and effective structure of public health programs. The world had never seen before so sharp and unmistakable a transformation. Now vast numbers of workers from temperate regions, such as the continental U.S., could work hard and long in this tropical climate with little fear of diseases that had once been dreaded scourges.

## THE PROBLEM OF THE TYPE OF CANAL

This preparatory period was also occupied by studies, discussions, and decisions as to the kind of canal to be built.

The final plan called for a multilevel lock type, rather than a sea-level canal. The actual crossing of the isthmus, a distance of some forty miles, would be made mostly on water standing about eighty-five feet above sea level.

This elevated waterway was to be created in part by damming

a river to form an artificial lake, and partly by excavating a great channel between lofty hills. Multiple locks were to be built to lift and lower ships by that eighty-five-foot difference.

In the United States, details of the completed plan were hailed with general satisfaction. This, it was stated and repeated many times, called for engineering and construction labors vaster than anything previously attempted in human history.

## CONSTRUCTING THE CANAL

The organization of the actual construction went through various stages and phases. At first, operations were headed by two civilian engineers, J. F. Wallace and John F. Stevens. Each served for a relatively short time, then resigned.

In 1907, President Theodore Roosevelt placed an army engineer, Colonel G. W. Goethals, in charge. He soon was given almost complete power over all aspects of work and living in the Canal Zone. A commission of expert consultants was retained, but its members had advisory, not executive, powers.

The American canal planners had expected originally that about ninety-five million cubic yards of material would have to be excavated. This was not much beyond the seventy-eight million cubic yards that had been excavated by the two French companies before the U.S. took over. Only a portion of the French excavation proved useful to the American canal design.

During 1908–1909, important plan changes raised to 175 million cubic yards the requirements for excavation. Yet this was not the end for the scores of tireless, puffing steam shovels that bit and scooped and gouged and dumped.

There were battles to come in which these power tools would be weapons against a malevolent environment.

Towering high above the eighty-five-foot channel level of the future canal was the formation called Cucaracha (Cockroach) Hill. It was not far from the site selected for the locks at the Pacific end of the canal.

Nearby, on the opposite side of the future channel, loomed the great hill called Culebra. Still another massive formation, Gold Hill, rose to 400 feet above the channel level.

Disaster struck in 1907 when a great earth slide down the Cucaracha slope forced the canal builders to remove an additional three million cubic yards of clay. Since one cubic yard includes twenty-seven cubic feet, this is clearly a staggering quantity.

Five years later, in 1912, titanic slippages took place again. One sent masses of material down the Culebra slope. Another took place diagonally across the channel. These setbacks added between thirteen and fourteen million cubic yards to the excavation necessary before the canal could be completed.

Battles such as these boosted the total excavations to about 232 million cubic yards. Thus, the actual digging out and hauling away for the high-level canal proved greater than that originally estimated by de Lesseps for a sea-level canal route!

Some observers came to fear that the incessant slides might never permit the canal to operate in safety. However, the engineers learned how to cut back until the slope angles were too gradual to start earth sliding again.

There was an abundance of heavy equipment to command. Steam shovels numbered more than 100. Railway equipment, in which the scooped-out earth was hauled away, included several hundred locomotives, thousands of cars designed to receive, carry, and dump dirt, and also dozens of spreaders and numbers of trackshifting devices.

All this equipment was essential. Excavation means not only taking dirt away, but also putting it someplace where it will either help or at least not harm the major work at hand.

The greatest single slippage battle was fought and finally won at Culebra Cut. Victory came only after 110 million cubic yards of material had been taken from that site. It was nearly half the total excavation for the entire Panama Canal!

About thirty separate slides took place during construction. Early in August 1914, channel and locks were completed and the first sea-going vessel passed completely through the canal. But the slides had not given up. Just over two months later, in mid-October, still another slippage tore down a slope and had to be dealt with.

During the first years of canal operation the channel through the Culebra Cut sector had a bottom width of at least 300 feet and a channel depth of at least forty-five feet. The slope down to the channel had been cut back so deeply and smoothly that future slides seemed most unlikely.

Yet the battle has never really been given up. Continual attention, repair, and improvement has been given to this critical sector which is now known as the Gaillard Cut, rather than Culebra. In 1966 the eight-mile length of the channel through this cut was widened from 300 to 500 feet, at a cost of about four million dollars. Illumination was installed so the great cut could be lighted after dark.

If all the excavation at the site of the present Panama Canal could be piled into one great mass of earth, it would suffice to form a wall around the world at the equator—a wall twenty feet thick and between twenty-three and twenty-five feet tall!

## THROUGH THE CANAL, STAGE BY STAGE

An average of over 1000 ships a month pass through the canal. They follow an interesting sequence of operations.

A vessel bound from the Caribbean Sea, Atlantic side, to the Pacific, actually enters the *channel* of the canal about five miles before it passes into the canal itself. This approach channel is dredged into the bottom of what might appear to a newcomer as open sea.

The vessel passes the city of Colón, Panama, on its left or port side. Then it reaches Cristobal, the Caribbean port, for the canal itself. From there it proceeds, under careful controls, in its further progress through the canal.

Many people think that the canal, since it joins Atlantic and Pacific oceans, must run due east and west. The curious curvature of that part of Central America, however, produces a very different direction, as the compass will verify. The Atlantic to Pacific crossing is, in fact, made in a *southeasterly* direction. The reverse crossing is, obviously, made in a *northwesterly* direction. The Pacific end of the canal, in short, lies actually to the east of the Atlantic end.

The vessel, after leaving Cristobal, continues on at sea level, until it reaches Gatun. There, in a series of three great locks, it is raised to the eighty-five-foot water level of Gatun Lake, the body of water formed by damming the Chagres River. Here the vessel floats above what was once the lower basin of the Chagres Valley.

The run through Gatun Lake is about twenty-three miles long. Next the vessel enters the narrower confines of the Gaillard Cut and travels an additional eight miles, still at the same elevated water level.

Then, at Pedro Miguel, comes the first downward step, in a lock with a thirty-foot drop. From here the vessel crosses the small Miraflores Lake, at about fifty-five feet over sea level. At the far end are the twin Miraflores locks. These lower the vessel to the level of the Pacific Ocean.

The concluding sector takes the vessel past the canal's Pacific port of Balboa and the nearby residential and administrative office area called Balboa Heights. On the left, or port side, as the vessel heads for the open sea, is the city of Panama which is not part of the Canal Zone.

The last phase of the crossing is made above another dredged out channel into the Bay of Panama, assuring safety for even deep-draught vessels.

Such a canal crossing totals about fifty miles from the limit of one approach channel to the other. About forty of these miles are within the canal itself, and just over thirty of those miles are at the eighty-five-foot level.


GIANT LOCKS OF THE PANAMA CANAL

More than a mile of such a vessel's movement through the canal takes place within the six great concrete boxes, or locks. Each has a maximum usable length of 1000 feet, a width of 110 feet, and a depth of 45 feet. Huge steel gates swing shut to close either or both ends of each lock.

These locks are all paired, providing two active waterways, side by side.

If all the twelve lock-boxes were laid end to end, they would extend 12,000 feet!

These locks were the most massive concrete structures ever built up to the time the canal began to operate in 1914—and for a good while afterwards.

A total of more than five million cubic yards of concrete was poured for the canal, of which about ninety percent went into the locks themselves.

Nearly one million tons of cement were mixed with sand, gravel, rock, and water to create these masses of artificial stone. It was called "a far greater achievement than the pyramids of Egypt" and was hailed as the most stupendous piece of engineering ever undertaken by man.

So massive is the concrete construction on the Gatun locks that steel reinforcing was found necessary only on certain portions. For the rest, the sheer bulk of concrete provided its own reinforcing effects.

Electricity, generated at Gatun, provided power for the many machines that operate the canal locks and other mechanisms. Striking among these are the unique electric towing locomotives that move the largest vessels steadily and safely into and out of the locks. The techniques of canal transit have been constantly refined and improved. Safety is a prime consideration at all stages.

During 1966 just over 12,600 vessels crossed via the canal. Their total tonnage came to between seventy-six and seventy-seven million tons. The totals they paid amounted to between seventy-two and seventy-three million dollars. Obviously, an average ton is carried through the canal for a fee of less than one dollar.


MILITARY ASPECTS OF THE CANAL

From the start, the canal has been operated as a part of the military establishment of the United States. An appointee of the President fills two posts at once: (1) governor of the Canal Zone, whose population of about 60,000 includes nearly 3000 U.S. employees engaged in various positions in the government of the zone. (2)

president of the company that operates the canal and also the railroad that serves the zone.

As Zone Governor, this official is responsible to the Secretary of the Army. As company president, he is responsible to a board of directors, who are also appointed by the Secretary of the Army.

Technical operations of the canal have run rather smoothly. Its political after-effects, however, have resulted in friction and conflicts between the U.S. and several other nations.

First came the question of tolls for the new U.S.-owned canal. Should the same rates be applied to ships of U.S. registry as to those under other flags? In 1912, even before the canal was completed, the Congress passed a measure to free coastwise U.S. shipping from canal tolls. Britain emphatically protested that this violated a valid agreement previously made by the United States to treat vessels of all nations equally.

Finally in 1914, under urging from President Woodrow Wilson, Congress reversed this action and authorized a schedule of equal canal charges for vessels of all nations.

A longer and more rankling complaint was that of the Republic of Colombia. It charged that in 1903 the United States had instigated, aided, and rewarded the "rebellion" that resulted in the breaking away of its former state, Panama. In the eyes of most of the rest of the world, Colombia's case against the giant of the north was strong.

Finally, in 1922, the United States paid twenty million dollars to Colombia as a kind of compensation for damages, and extended certain privileges in the way of land transportation. Colombia, in return, agreed to recognize the independence of Panama.

The original treaty by which Panama had turned over the Canal Zone to the U. S. had provided that the U. S. was to pay an annual rental of $250,000 for the complete use and control of that zone. This amount was increased afterwards, and the United States agreed also to restrict American business activities in the zone to those directly concerned with canal shipping.

Still, the presence of U.S. soldiers and the exercise of American control over an important area cutting across their country, irritated many Panamanians. A new treaty, signed in 1955, increased to nearly two million dollars a year the annual payments to Panama, and turned over to Panama certain land and buildings not needed by the canal administration. Further, a pledge was included that within the zone equal pay and equal opportunity would be given to all employees, whether of U.S. or other citizenship. This was designed to offer greater opportunities to Panamanian citizens employed or seeking employment in the Canal Zone.

As a further concession, the United States agreed to provide a high bridge across the Pacific entrance to the canal, thus closing a gap in the great Inter-American highway.

Completed in autumn, 1962, this Thatcher Ferry Bridge arches over the canal near Balboa at a height of about 200 feet above the water level. It is approximately a mile long, has four traffic lanes and includes three spans.

A little more than a year later, anti-American feeling kindled a serious outbreak among Panamanians. Demanding an end to sole U.S. sovereignty over this strip of Panamanian soil, numbers of Panamanian citizens demonstrated. Clashes followed in which twenty-one or more Panamanians were killed and also three U.S. soldiers.

Seeking to pacify the situation, the Presidents of the United States and Panama issued a joint declaration in April 1964. It called for peaceful negotiations to settle the disputed issues. Before the end of 1964, President Lyndon B. Johnson proposed that a new treaty be negotiated for the use of the Canal Zone by the United States. Such a treaty, it was clear, would be more favorable to Panama than the present one.

At the same time, the White House announced the intention of the U.S. government to build still another interocean canal—a sea-level structure this time, whose route might either lie elsewhere in Panama, or in Colombia, Nicaragua, or Costa Rica. Thus the world may yet see a sea-level type canal between the Atlantic and Pacific.

Among the present "independent agencies" maintained by the federal government there is a small but significant group called the Atlantic-Pacific Interoceanic Canal Study Commission.

The plans and projects that are within its scope of study may lead to a canal that overshadows the Panama Canal, now in its second half-century of operation. Estimated total cost of the Panama Canal was $375 million. Today's steeply increased costs for materials and construction would doubtless make this seem a very small splash compared with the costs of a future sea-level canal.

Among the factors favoring the sea-level canal today is the great speed in transit that becomes possible when no locks or only entrance-exit locks are required. Beyond a doubt, any second canal would be constructed so as to be large enough to pass the greatest aircraft carriers now afloat or under consideration. The Panama Canal was not designed large enough for the largest ships of our time.

Thus it may be that the late twentieth century will bring into being the same kind of sea-level link that Ferdinand de Lesseps proposed to build when he first organized support for the unfortunate Panama adventure in the 1880s.

## THE SIGHTSEER IN PANAMA TODAY

Tourist constantly visit Panama. Many come by air. One of the principal appeals is to watch the canal in action. From Panama City to Colón one can travel by automobile in about an hour. The road weaves through jungles aflame with bougainvillea and hibiscus flowers and wavy with graceful banana trees.

On the way, the road crosses the Continental Divide, the backbone of the continents, which can be traced even here in slender Central America. The sightseer may pause at the Gatun Lake Lookout. From there he can watch, far below, the ships moving along the jungle-bordered Panama Canal.

Panama in our time is a place of striking contrasts. Here, in this tropical isthmus, where once the famed buccaneer Henry Morgan and his men marched inland seeking gold, one can see in Panama City luxury hotels and gambling casinos for wealthy visitors and, not far away, the huts of the poor native families with naked children playing in the ill-kept yards.

# XII

## THE EMPIRE STATE BUILDING

## MAMMOTH OF MANHATTAN

Numberless crowded streets—high growths of iron,
   slender, strong, light, splendidly uprising
   toward clear skies . . .
The free city! no slaves! no owners of slaves!
The beautiful city, the city of hurried and
   sparkling waters! the city of spires and masts!

—WALT WHITMAN, *Mannahatta*

The world's tallest inhabited structure and the towering land-mark that looms over the island of Manhattan is the Empire State Building. It has been called "the eighth wonder of the modern world."

It was designated in 1955 by the American Society of Civil Engineers as one of their seven chosen modern American marvels of engineering, in recognition of the vast problems faced and overcome in its construction. Thus it became the companion, on that list chosen by experts, of two great dams, the Grand Coulee and the Hoover Dam, a mighty bridge system, the San Francisco-Oakland Bay Bridge, and three giant systems involving water, the Panama Canal, the Colorado Aqueduct, and the City of Chicago sewage disposal system.

Among all these seven choices, only the Empire State Building is an enterprise privately owned, privately financed, and privately managed.

Each year about two million people, including visitors from far corners of the earth, ride one of its more than seventy elevators to reach the observation platforms of the building. One is at the eighty-sixth floor level, the other at the 102nd. They are open all day long until midnight, every day of the year. With clear weather, visibility may extend from thirty to fifty miles. Sometimes it is possible to see ships in motion far out on the Atlantic Ocean.

Closer at hand is spread the spectacular vista of the City of New York as seen from so far above its streets.

From its base, facing on Fifth Avenue in busy midtown New York, to the tip of its needle-like TV tower, the Empire State Build-

191

ing rises 1,472 feet. It is so tall that one elevator cannot be run all the way from its main floor to its top towers. To reach the observation points, it is necessary to change elevators, transferring at the eightieth floor.

The Empire State Building has become a spectacular experience for sightseers; a busy humming center of more than 900 businesses or professional offices; and as much a symbol of the City of New York as the Eiffel Tower is of Paris.

In addition to all these, through its great TV and radio broadcasting facilities it now reaches out into the day and night lives of several millions of people. The twenty-two-story tower antenna, added to the top of the building in 1951, serves nine commercial television stations—two of them UHF (ultra-high frequency) and seven VHF (very high frequency). Additional TV stations are expected to be served in the future.

The newest addition to this colossus of modern communication is a "master FM antenna", the only one of its kind in the world. It was constructed on top of the building in 1965, and enables the programs of up to seventeen separate FM stations to be broadcast at the same time from this single center of radio transmission.

A few TV transmission masts have been erected in the United States whose tops do outreach the tip of the Empire State Building —but none of these serve to shelter human activity or residence. They are simply enormous girders, guyed by cables so they will stand erect and lift their transmitting elements to dizzy heights above the surface of the earth.

Among such masts built solely for TV transmission are those at Fargo, North Dakota (KTHI—2063 feet); Knoxville, Tennessee (WBIR—1749 feet); Columbus, Georgia (WTVN and WRBL— also 1749 feet); Cape Girardeau, Missouri (KFVS—1676 feet); Portland, Maine (WGAN—1619 feet); and Oklahoma City (the KWTV mast—1572 feet).

The Empire State Building was planned and built before the first regular TV programs were broadcast. In fact, it was built in 1930-1931, years of the great depression, when unemployment and want were rising in the United States. The original cost was $40,948,000.

The TV transmission "needle" cost an additional three million dollars.

In 1965, the Empire State Building was sold for sixty-five million dollars—the greatest sum ever paid for a single building. Principal purchasers were the Lawrence A. Wien Syndicate and the Prudential Insurance Company.


HOW IT BEGAN

In 1799 on the island of Manhattan a man by the name of John Thompson advertised his twenty-acre farm for sale. He suggested in this announcement that the rapid growth of New York City would greatly enhance the value of the property in years to come.

That farm included the area that now fronts on Fifth Avenue between Thirty-fourth and Thirty-fifth streets. For the farm, Thompson received $7000.

In the 1800s the land was acquired by John Jacob Astor who built two different mansions on its site. They became centers of New York social life.

The last of these Astor mansions was removed during the late 1890s. On the same location was built the Waldorf-Astoria Hotel. It became world famous as the meeting place of New York's high society—the so-called "Four Hundred." During thirty-five years the Waldorf-Astoria was the great city's most fashionable and aristocratic hotel. Its banquets, balls, and receptions were regarded as the last word in elegance and opulence.

Even before the Waldorf-Astoria moved to a location further uptown, a group of businessmen, confident that the site could become a future center of profitable commercial activity, began investigating the possibilities for replacing the hotel with a giant office building.

The group was headed by the leaders of two of the nation's

largest corporations—John J. Raskob of General Motors Corporation, and Pierre S. du Pont of the E. I. du Pont de Nemours giant chemical company. As its titular head, the group chose the colorful and popular Alfred E. Smith. He had served four times as Governor of New York State and had been the Democratic Party's candidate for the U. S. Presidency in 1928.

Now "Al" Smith occupied an impressive suite of offices as President of Empire State, Incorporated, which was to erect the future skyscraper.

CONSTRUCTION OF THE EMPIRE
STATE BUILDING

Purchase of the old Waldorf-Astoria and the land on which it stood cleared the way for important decisions on the design, the dimensions, and the costs of the building to be erected there.

The Waldorf-Astoria was removed completely in an impressive wrecking operation that required five months' time. Then began the work of excavating foundations suitable for a lofty skyscraper.

The decision had been to construct a true giant of a building. As the specifications were spelled out in terms of materials required, the size and scope of the coming structure became evident.

In addition to the structural steel skeleton, its other requirements were enormous. Here are some of them: ten million bricks to be laid, though few would be visible from outside or in; about 750 tons of aluminum and stainless steel for outer walls; pipes for plumbing to total about 60 miles in length; 1,670,000 cubic feet of concrete to be poured; 200,000 cubic feet of stone to be laid.

Beside this, the completed building was to be heated by more than 6600 radiators, provided with telephone connections by wiring totaling more than fifteen million feet in length, and supplied with fresh air from the outside by blower systems that could "inhale" nearly 17,000 cubic feet of clean atmosphere per *second*.

The volume of the completed Empire State Building would be thirty-six million cubic feet.

It has been calculated that if all the materials needed for the original construction of the building were to have been delivered in one single shipment, they would have filled a freight train fifty-seven miles long.

A brisk tempo marked the entire progress of construction. As soon as the Waldorf-Astoria's remains had been hauled away in some 16,000 truckloads, the foundation-diggers went to work with power and hand equipment, and within three months, by mid-March, 1930, had cleared the fifty-five foot "hole" for the future basement and sub-basement. Nearly a quarter of a million cubic feet of dirt and more than four and one-half million cubic feet of rock were removed in the process.

April was just one week under way when the first steel beams began to lift toward the sky over Manhattan.

The rise of the Empire State Building was rapid, thanks to a series of bold and well-planned innovations in construction methods. One of the most striking was the elimination of the traditional wheelbarrows in carrying materials from the ground to the construction levels where they were to be used. In their place, small cars were used that ran on portable, narrow-gauge tracks.

The building materials were loaded into such cars in the basement, rolled into elevators fitted with similar tracks, and sped up to the floor-level where they were needed. There, the cars were rolled off onto tracks that had already been laid completely around the skeleton steelwork on that floor.

Each car could carry 400 bricks, four times the capacity of the familiar wheelbarrows.

These and similar methods of pre-planning resulted in the rise of the steel skeleton at an average rate of five and one half stories per week—just about one story, on the average, per working day. In fact, during just one autumn day in 1930 the building rose by fourteen stories! This included not only the steel skeleton itself but also the other essentials—trim, concrete, stonework, and so on.

The entire giant steel skeleton was riveted, from foundation to tower top, within the span of 161 days—well under half a year.

The sequence of operations could be watched, with the help of binoculars, from the street or from nearby buildings. The topmost operations were those of the "high-iron" workers, or erection crews. They steered into temporary position the huge columns and beams, hoisted by the five great derricks. These positions were secured, for the time, by bolts—and then the high-iron men moved on to put together the floor above.

Now came the riveting gangs whose members numbered hundreds. They worked in groups of five, four of whom functioned to make possible the noisy, battering blows of the riveter with his pneumatic gun. A heater, using a stove, brought the rivet to the red-hot state that meant the steel would be plastic, then tossed it with tongs through the air to a catcher with bucket or steel glove. He passed it to the bucker-up who inserted it into the proper hole and then backed it up while the riveter smashed flat its extended end with a loud burst of blows by his gun. The last member of the team was the helper, also called the punk.

At levels below this ritual of riveting, other skilled workers were laying-in concrete, stone, and metal trim. In the Empire State Building the concrete, for example, was held firm by about three million square feet of steel mesh reinforcing.

The exterior skin of the building is formed from limestone and granite. From its sixth floor to the top it is trimmed in stainless steel. As the building rose, floor by floor, the installation crews fastened securely in place plates of dull-silver aluminum between the top of each window and the sill of the window on the floor above.

This pattern of metal inserts, rather than granite and limestone between windows, adds immensely to the soaring lines of the great structure. In all, a total of some 600,000 pounds of stainless-steel window trim and 900,000 pounds of aluminum plates were thus incorporated into the skyscraper.

Its 6500 windows were designed to be set flush, rather than being set back into the masonry, as had been customary before.

All this had to be accomplished in the midst of the congested streets of Manhattan. Speed in construction was essential, not only to lessen the additional crowding and traffic tangles in those streets but also to keep down labor costs.

Whenever possible, work was done beforehand away from the

building site, and then brought there to be assembled into the rising structure. Also, the building's simplicity of design permitted some standardized parts to be prefabricated and used interchangeably, instead of being handmade at each location in the building itself.

Systematic simplicity governed also the supply and delivery of the structural steel and other materials. Two contractors, the American Bridge Company and McClintic-Marshall, erected the skeleton. Together they set up a supply lot in Bayonne, New Jersey. There the great steel members were delivered from the mills in Pittsburgh, and sorted and marked to show just where each piece was to be placed in the rising structure.

Beams and girders, as needed, were then towed in barges across the Hudson River, loaded on trucks at piers on Nineteenth and Twenty-third streets, and then trucked by way of Thirty-third Street to the destination.

Material supply was kept continuous and swift. On one occasion as little as eighteen hours elapsed between the time certain pieces of structural steel left the Pittsburgh mill and the time that they were placed in position at the building site.

Problems of men as well as materials were solved as the great work went forward. During the hot summer months the construction workers became thirsty, as well as hungry. Much time would be lost if they had to be lowered to ground level to eat and to drink.

Miles of temporary water pipe were laid in the huge 60,000-ton steel frame to raise cool drinking water to the workers. Cafeterias were set up at various levels—the third, the ninth, the twenty-fourth, the forty-seventh, and the sixty-fourth floors. Thus refreshing water and food followed the construction gangs as they moved skyward.

Four passenger elevators had been salvaged from the demolition of the old Waldorf-Astoria Hotel. These were put to use in temporary installations and carried the 3500 construction workers to their tasks on the rising floors, with minimum time loss.

Accidents could delay work and lose valuable manpower. Hence safety procedures were emphasized and enforced. A modern hospital, staffed with doctors and nurses and complete with emergency operating room was maintained in the base of the growing structure.

## THE BUILDING IS COMPLETED

On May 1, 1931, the Empire State Building was officially finished and inaugurated. President Herbert Hoover pressed a button
in Washington that turned on its lights.

Some 3500 men had labored one year plus forty-five days to erect
this 365,000 ton record-breaker among the world's buildings. More
remarkable than the relative speed of its construction was the fact,
rare in the annals of major building projects, that the cost when
completed had been less—not more—than the preliminary estimates.
In fact, the final cost proved to be between fifteen and twenty percent below those earlier computations. This saving was caused not
solely by the time- and labor-saving methods that had been used, but
also in part by the fact that the increasing economic depression was
reducing many prices and labor costs below what might have been
expected in good times.

In greeting the completed building, some commentators noted
that though it towered to a height more than three times that of
of the Great Pyramid of Khufu at Giza, Egypt, it had been built
in about one-twentieth of the time—and by a labor force about one-
thirtieth the number of the 100,000 men that Khufu was reputed
to have kept at work during a score of years.

Not all observers were enthusiastic, however. There had been
many scoffers during the planning and building stages. Many a
dark forecast was made for its financial future. In fact, during the
continuing depression years that followed its first opening, these
pessimists seemed to be right. The building was less than one third
occupied when it opened. The Manhattan wits delighted in nick-
naming it "The Empty State Building."

Actually, about ten years of operation went by before it was fully
occupied. Its total annual rent receipts are estimated to reach about
ten million dollars a year.

There were other doubts that the Empire State Building encountered. Some, not including expert engineers, doubted that so tall a
building could safely support its own weight and face the strains
that it must experience. Design and construction provide a great

safety factor. On each floor special "pressure-relieving" connections were installed. These made use of the heavy, soft metal lead to give an additional flexibility and resilience to the steel skeleton.

That skeleton today, bearing the full weight of the building and its contents, shows a remarkable response. The height of the building is actually about one-half foot less than the sums of the lengths of the separate vertical steel members riveted together to reach its top. The building is compressed or squeezed together that much by its own weight.

Thus, the tip of the TV tower stands 1,472 feet above Fifth Avenue, rather than about 1,472 and one-half feet. This was no surprise to the engineers, however. They knew well in advance that structural steel has a "give" when placed under compression.

Another source of concern to some observers was the question of what such a lofty building would do under the force of the strong winds that sometimes sweep over Manhattan. Here too the answer is simple and reassuring. The steel gives slightly, without endangering its strength in any way.

As a matter of fact, careful measurements indicate that in strong winds of sixty to ninety miles an hour speed, the summit of the great structure is shifted by less than a foot in the direction that the wind is blowing. This does not mean that it remains motionless, however. Like any elastic rod or reed, it oscillates very slightly under the effect of the wind flow. This oscillation is quite small—a total distance of two inches or less—and it is also quite slow. A full cycle of such to-and-fro motion is completed in about fifteen to twenty seconds.

This wind-produced vibration has a scope relatively no greater than if a rod about the height of a man should be inclined about one-twentieth of an inch, and should vibrate over a distance of about one-hundredth of an inch!

## THE RACE TO REACH UPWARD

The Empire State Building was designed throughout with the aim of outreaching all competing office buildings. Its emphasis on the upward lines by means of the aluminum plates placed between the glass in the columns of windows, accentuates the vertical. The total effect is one of loftiness and noble simplicity.

Only the lower floors occupy the full size of the site. Starting with the sixth floor, the building is set back sixty feet from its base. Several setbacks at higher levels appear. Then the massive tower itself begins its rise to the eighty-fifth floor.

How was the great tower to terminate? That question was settled rather late—and there is an interesting tale to tell about the final plan for topping off the tower. It involves the rivalry between the builders of the Empire State Building and of the nearby Chrysler Building, also constructed during 1929–1930.

Actually, three buildings were involved in a rather fantastic contest to outreach all previous records. The Bank of Manhattan Building at 40 Wall Street was designed first for 47 stories. Then W. P. Chrysler, of the automobile corporation that bears his name, acquired a Lexington Avenue location and a set of plans for what had been known until then as the future Reynolds Building. The race to reach upward was under way.

A total of twenty-four additional stories were added to plans for the Bank of Manhattan Building. By the time it was completed, it reached, with the help of an extra-tall flagpole on top, to a height of 925 feet.

This would have bested the Chrysler Building by about eighty feet. Mr. Chrysler came up with a new topping for his structure— a so-called *finial* tower of curiously curving and overlapping metal plates. This spikelike addition boosted the summit of his building to just 1030 feet, safely higher than the Bank of Manhattan flagpole peak and higher even than the top of the Eiffel Tower.

Under this gleaming metallic headdress, the Chrysler Building has sixty-six real stories and six penthouse stories, or seventy-two floor levels in all.

When the news became final that the Empire State Building would include eighty-six floors, those close to the construction field expected that it would certainly challenge and very likely surpass the Chrysler Building in height. However, it was not known just how this final reach upward would be accomplished.

That became clear with the revelation of the decision to construct at the very top a so-called dirigible "mooring mast." This afterthought, or addition, to the basic building design is a great 600-ton steel superstructure rising 200 feet above the 1050 foot height of the building itself.

The airships were to be moored, supposedly, near its top, which stood now 1250 feet above the street, safely taller than any other building or self-supported tower then on earth.

It is through this mooring mast that one ascends today to the 102nd story for the higher of the two observatories in the Empire State Building. The round top of this mast, though it appears slender enough from the street below, is thirty-two feet in diameter.

Mr. Raskob and his associates reached for, and secured for some years to come, the prestige of the tallest structure.

Those who knew something about winds, weather, and the ways of airships hardly took seriously the continued reference to this addition as a genuine mooring mast. Nevertheless, that fiction was clung to for quite some time. One attempt was even made to attach an airship there—not even a large rigid dirigible, but a small nonrigid blimp. It almost led to disaster. An updraft very nearly overturned it, and the participants narrowly escaped with their lives.

Pedestrians on New York's streets far below were puzzled that day by a sudden downpour without warning of rain. It was the water ballast from the blimp, dumped abruptly on the city street.

Since then, the mooring mast remains one in name only, and its form has become part of the familiar contour of the most striking landmark in the incredible skyline of overcrowded Manhattan.

## A SPECTACULAR CRASH

Many years later, on July 28, 1945, the Empire State Building was the scene of a fantastic and tragic crash. A B-25 Air Force bomber, astray in a fog, crashed into the great tower between its seventy-eighth and seventy-ninth floors. Three people aboard the plane and ten in the building were killed, while twenty-five others were injured.

The structural damage to the building itself was found to be slight.

Today, the top thirty floors of the building are illuminated at night by powerful floodlights placed on various setbacks of the structure. The great tower is bathed in a radiance of 125-million candle-power. These lights are turned on at dusk and shine throughout the night.

Red aircraft warning-lights glow vividly also on the great television tower above the mooring mast.

The floodlights are turned off, however, during periods of bird migration, in response to the request of the National Audubon Society. This is an attempt to prevent the migrating birds from being blinded by light and dashing themselves to death against the tower in their confusion.

## THE GREAT TOWER AND TV

When the first announcements of an Empire State Building plan were made, television was unknown and undreamed-of except by a few advanced technicians who could command little attention.

The race to make the top of the building so high was not connected with any anticipation that some day it might serve as a great transmitting center for such an advanced method of communication. Soon after it was completed, however, the building and television became notably connected.

Within six months after the Empire State Building officially opened its doors, a laboratory went to work near the top of its tower to make experiments on possible ways to transmit moving pictures by means of wireless waves. By 1941, the first commercial TV show was transmitted.

Further progress was largely held up by World War II and its aftermaths. Meanwhile the development of radar and microwaves added enormously to the techniques available to television transmission. By 1949 the principal TV broadcasters needed effective transmission facilities to reach the great mass audience in Manhat-

tan and surrounding city areas. They agreed to build for their joint use a still loftier structure on top of the Empire State mooring mast. This TV transmitter needle was designed to rise 220 feet higher. Its total weight—about 120,000 pounds. It was constructed at that dizzy height during a ten-month period that came to a triumphant end in May, 1951.

Beside the multiple TV and FM transmission facilities, it provides a lightning rod. Those who know, say that in the thunderstorms that surge over the island of Manhattan this protective device has been hit by lightning hundreds of times, without any injury to the lofty structure.

## INSIDE THE TALLEST OF BUILDINGS

What one sees of the outside of the Empire State Building, and the surrounding sights that one can see from its observation towers, are both so memorable that the actual interior of the office building itself sometimes does not receive its share of attention.

The building entrance is imposing, rising to a height of four stories. The lobby itself reaches the equivalent of three stories to its ceiling. It is lined with marble originating in France, Italy, Belgium, and Germany.

The tides of human traffic to and from this structure are tremendous. Each typical working day brings an estimated 35,000 different people into the building. Some are there to work in the offices, others to visit and do business in them, still others as sightseers and tower-gazers.

Nine moving stairways or escalators lift passengers from the lower lobby below the main floor to the second floor area. There are, of course, stationary stairways all the way from the ground level to the 102nd floor. These, with a total of 1860 separate steps, represent a challenge to especially hardy climbers!

The Empire State Building houses a large community. Their needs give rise to some interesting figures. It is estimated that the 16,000 office workers use about two million paper cups each year. Each month an average of 100 tons of trash must be removed. It is collected daily, compressed in an automatic baling machine, tied up, and hauled away.

About 18,000 telephone instruments are in use throughout the building, with telephone and telegraph cable lines extending about 3500 miles in all.

Keeping the building clean, inside and out, and maintaining it in good repair represent a gigantic complex of tasks. Daily, 200 people travel through the structure, doing nothing other than cleaning its 1.8 million square feet of office space, its 280,000 square feet of public corridors, its 37,000 square feet of lavatories, and its extensive elevators and stairways.

In 1962, a huge job of cleaning the outside of the Empire State Building was carried through. Crews traveled on electrically moved scaffolds, suspended by cables. They scrubbed, painted, and waterproofed during a six-month period from spring to fall. It was one of the world's most extensive spring cleanings!

A constant task is that of keeping the structure's 6500 windows clean. Each window is washed twice a month. The washers form a crew who qualify for a kind of combat pay because of the hazards they face high above the city streets. On the upper floors, during days of high winds the gusts blow up rather than down. On these floors the window-washers have learned, in reverse of the usual sequence, to wash first the lower half of a window, and then the upper half.

This small city, sited on a single foundation and reaching so far into the air imposes an endless round of attention and tasks on the personnel assigned to keep it clean year round, warm in winter, cool in summer, served with water, electricity, sanitation, communications, and all the other complex necessities and conveniences of our era.

### HIGHER STILL?

Plans have been announced to build a still taller building on the island of Manhattan—a twin-towered World Trade Center for the Port of New York. Both in architectural design and engineering concepts it promises to blaze new trails.

Its planned 110 stories would reach to a height of 1350 feet, 100 feet taller than the 102nd floor observatory of the Empire State Building, though not taller than the tip of the towering TV needle above it.

Even with a World Trade Center looming near the lower end of Manhattan, it seems likely that the Empire State Building will retain its imperial hold on the skyline of the nation's metropolis and the memories of those who visit it.

# XIII

## GRAND COULEE DAM

---

## GREATEST STRUCTURE
## OF MAN-MADE STONE

. . . one modulated
Eagle's cry made stone, stopping the strength of the sea . . .

—ROBINSON JEFFERS, *Cawdor*

The largest man-made construction of concrete in the world stands in the central section of the state of Washington, in the United States. It is larger by far than the Pyramid of Khufu. But unlike the pyramids, which were built to house and care for the spirit of man after death, this gigantic masonry is a giver of life and fertility, a producer of abundance and prosperity to land which might otherwise be a barren, rugged wilderness.

Like the ziggurats of Babylon and the great pyramids of Egypt, this construction, too, is related closely to a great river—the Columbia River. It blocks the river's former channel from bank to bank as the river flows southwest from Canada in a twisting course.

This is the Grand Coulee Dam. It is higher than a 46-story building, it is as long as 12 city blocks, and its weight is 22 million tons. It has created a waterfall which, at its peak, is half as wide, though twice as high, as Niagara Falls, and it has formed Lake Franklin D. Roosevelt, 151 miles long with 600 miles of shoreline.

Its present power output of almost two million kilowatts makes it the second largest single hydroelectric power center in the world. The Soviet Union's great dam at Bratsk has a rated capacity of 3.8 million kilowatts. The Grand Coulee Dam, within the next 25 years will very likely be provided with additional generating capacity, raising its output to more than nine million kilowatts and assuring it of first place among sources of hydroelectric power in the world today.

Its goal in water supply to agriculture is similarly huge—nothing less than the irrigation of more than one million acres of land!

Enormous, too, are the costs involved. When its third hydroelectric power plant has been added, total costs of the Grand Coulee project will be close to $1,500,000,000.

Its size is staggering. It contains nearly 286 million cubic feet of concrete—or 10,590,000 cubic yards, as engineers usually measure such bulk. Many dams have a far greater volume, but these are earth or rock-fill dams. Notable among these is the Fort Peck Dam in Montana with a volume of 125,628,000 cubic yards.

Enough material has gone into the dam's construction to build 275 edifices the size of the Washington Monument, and enough concrete to build a two-lane highway twenty-two feet wide and eight inches thick, with a three-foot pedestrian walk, from Seattle to Miami.

It is a gravity dam, depending on its weight to prevent pressure from the water on its upstream face from tipping it over or causing it to slide.

The dam towers over two seemingly small powerhouses at its base. Each is actually as tall as a thirteen-story office building.

In 1965, Congress approved a bill to build a third Grand Coulee powerhouse under direction of the Department of the Interior. Under way and awaiting approval by Congress are plans for six additional giant generators to go into this third power plant. In addition to these, the plant will provide space for still another set of six generators.

When all twelve of these generators are completed and in action —possibly by 1992—Grand Coulee's total power output will be 9.2 million kilowatts. It would then be greater than the combined present electric outputs of Grand Coulee, Hoover, Shasta, Oake, Robert Moses-Niagara, St. Lawrence, and Chief Joseph power projects.

In power generation, size usually spells savings. Secretary of the Interior Stewart L. Udall on January 13, 1967, said that the Grand Coulee "will be the cheapest hydroelectric capacity that can be installed anywhere in the United States."

The electrical power and irrigation benefits furnished by the Grand Coulee Dam and the related projects of the Columbia River Basin reach into the far corners of the Pacific Northwest and affect directly and indirectly the people of the entire United States and even, through industry and trade, the people of other nations.

IN THE BEGINNING

Sixty million years ago, deep within the earth, was formed the granite rock on which the Grand Coulee Dam now rests. Through millions of years following, wind and water erosion and movements in the earth's crust gradually brought to the surface this mighty rock. Slowly a river drainage system was established, flowing from what is now Canada south into the State of Washington, and eventually west toward the Pacific Ocean.

From time to time, enormous quantities of basalt lava, traveling from a distance of thirty to fifty miles within the depths of the earth, broke through cracks and fissures in the earth's surface. These lava flows spread over the eastern part of the state of Washington and into Idaho and Oregon, forming a vast plain which remains part of the landscape of that part of the country today.

The lava outpourings, however, disrupted the southward course of the streams and diverted them instead toward the west. Thus the present Columbia River system was formed.

Then came the Ice Age, about a million years ago. An enormous ice sheet, born in the Canadian Arctic, spread southward, covering with ice all but the peaks of the tallest mountains. It blocked the Columbia River at the point where the Grand Coulee Dam stands today, diverting its course.

In fact, an old-time native of the area, attorney William M. Clapp, one of the most active of those who dreamed and planned for a dam to harness the power of the river and bring fertility to the land, is quoted: "If the Almighty can dam up the Columbia with a cake of ice, man can do it with a piece of concrete."

As the ice melted, new streams and rivers dug new courses. New waterfalls were created and the waters surged over formerly dry areas covering them with a mixture of basalt debris carried by the melting glacial waters and icebergs. With the melting of the ice also, the river resumed its former course. The gorge, created by glacial action, now called the Grand Coulee, was left dry, and the surrounding land arid and unsuited to growth of life-giving plants.

It is a long stretch of history from the Grand Coulee Dam back to man's first attempts to bring water to dry, unproductive lands. Some six thousand years ago, men bailed water from the Tigris and Euphrates rivers in Mesopotamia, and out of the Nile in Egypt and poured it into their fields. Later came small canals to divert water from the rivers into more distant fields. Gradually, the canals became large enough for boats, and even crude machinery appeared for lifting the waters onto the fields. Some of these inefficient machines are still used in China, India, and Egypt. Storage wells or tanks are common in India today.

The next steps were low dams built across rivers to save the waters for the dry season—the forerunner of the giant dam of today.

## EARLY SETTLERS

The Grand Coulee Dam is situated about ninety miles west of Spokane in the State of Washington in the northwest corner of the United States.

Before white men went west and settled in what was then known as the Washington Territory, Indian tribes, somewhere around the beginning of the nineteenth century, were already making use of irrigation to cultivate their fields of potatoes and corn. These Columbia River Indians got water for their lands from a creek running down a canyon, near the present site of the town of Ephrata.

Fur trappers from Canada next penetrated northeast Washington, and between 1807 and 1821 the Canadian North West Company held a monopoly on Indian trading and fur trapping in the Columbia Basin area.

The Canadians were followed by American fur traders, missionaries, and settlers. For 25 years they continued to trickle into the area until, in 1846, a treaty with Great Britain gave that territory to the United States.

Now, more and more settlers arrived with the gold rush of 1855–1856 at Colville, adding to the population.

Conflicts arose with the Indians over claims to land, disputes being partly resolved when Indian reservations were established at Colville and Spokane.

During the period when the Territory was being settled and the railroads were pushing west, water had become more and more of a problem.

In 1898, a joint venture of the Great Northern Railway and the Co-operative Irrigation Company made an early attempt to irrigate the Columbia Basin area. The plan was to use the water from Brook Lake to irrigate a small area between Ephrata and Stratford. The venture failed as did many others following.

Some of the projects actually succeeded in delivering water to various areas, but the high costs of pumping and the low returns brought the projects to an end.

When the early part of the twentieth century brought large numbers of homesteaders into the Big Bend area of the Columbia River Basin, the agricultural development of the area became a problem. Dry farming of cereal grains had begun, but it was apparent that irrigation was the only solution for a growing, producing community.

Farmers had to rely on the scant rainfall to grow crops, and often this rainfall came at the wrong time of the year. Crops withered and died. The exodus out of the Basin grew. By 1910 population had dropped ten percent and in the ten years between 1920–1930, there was a further loss of thirty percent of the farmers. When business dwindled, the townspeople followed the exodus.

Bunchgrass and sagebrush once more took over the fields and swayed in the searing winds. Abandoned, crumbling houses and rusty windmills without water dotted the area.

Today, the Dam, pumping water from its reservoir over the rim of the canyon and into the Grand Coulee, irrigates the land which, in 1933, had been characterized by one of its few resident ranchers as being "known mostly for wheat, heat, and rattlesnakes."


EARLY PLANS

Who were the dreamers, the far-seeing ones, who laid the groundwork and planned and worked to turn their land into the fertile, thriving area it is today?

Billie Clapp, the man who visualized a dam instead of an ice sheet across the river was one. Though people in the area had talked and planned for years, he backed the idea with engineering investigation.

He and others argued that the dry gorge called Grand Coulee, once the temporary bed of the Columbia River, had come about when a glacier from the Arctic had blocked the river and diverted the Columbia's direction. Then, why could not a concrete dam block the stream, raise its level, and divert its waters once more down through the Grand Coulee?

The county commissioners at the time thought it a wild-sounding scheme, but agreed to a survey of the area. The report of the survey showed the plan had merit. Further studies were necessary.

In the meantime, a different plan was conceived and proposed by the chairman of the State Public Service Commission, E. F. Blaine. He proposed that water be transported to the Columbia Basin via a waterway system coming all the way from Pend Oreille Lake in Idaho, 130 miles away. His plans called for a dam to be built across the Pend Oreille River near Albeni Falls in Idaho. Through a succession of canals, natural waterways, viaducts, siphons, and reservoirs, the water was to be distributed to the land in the Basin.

But these rival plans were opposed by the groups who feared that cultivation of the Basin would wreck the price structure of the farm products. They also argued that the cost of construction was too high.

In 1919, the Columbia Basin Commission was created by the Washington State Legislature. It made studies of the two plans, finally recommending the waterway-Idaho system. But this was not the end.

Back and forth went the opinions and decisions. Report after report was submitted to the commission.

It is interesting to note that one of the men called upon by the commission for a report on the waterway plans was Major General George W. Goethals. Major Goethals was the man who built the Panama Canal.

There followed the self-sacrificing devotion of James O'Sullivan, an attorney in the area, who was convinced of the feasibility of the Grand Coulee plan. Finally, through the efforts of Senators Wesley L. Jones and Clarence C. Dill from the State of Washington, a major appropriation was called for by Congress to finance a study of the Columbia River area.

Work on the survey began in 1928 and was completed in 1931. Major John S. Butler of the Army Engineers, who investigated both proposed projects, reported the plan for the dam at Grand Coulee to be "altogether feasible, both from an economic and an engineering viewpoint. . . ."

Two events added to the necessity to push ahead with plans for irrigation and power. First, in the winter of 1929–1930, a power shortage brought about by drought crippled the area.

The second event was the exodus of the much-needed topsoil from the Pacific Northwest. This occurred in April, 1931. Passengers aboard a Honolulu-bound vessel, some 600 miles off the west coast, were suddenly engulfed in a huge dust cloud about 700 miles long. The soil was being blown off the land! Irrigation was sorely needed.

The country was in the midst of a depression and Congress was not willing to expend the huge sums needed to build the dam. President Herbert Hoover felt it was "inadvisable."

"We do not need further additions to our agricultural lands at present," he said in a message to Congress in February, 1932.

Soon after the election of Franklin D. Roosevelt as President of the United States, the vision became a reality. In a move to strike at the growing unemployment in this country, he created the Public Works Administration program and included the Grand Coulee Dam in its projects. The job of building the dam was given to the Bureau of Reclamation, under the Department of the Interior. Frank A. Banks was put in charge of the project as construction engineer.

On September 9, 1933, the first stakes were driven on the axis for the dam.

It had been some sixteen years since that summer day of 1917, in Billie Clapp's office, when the idea had been born. One of the group of local men, sitting around at that time discussing the food and water problems of the area, had suggested the water could come from the Columbia River at Grand Coulee. Clapp and his fellow residents took it from there. So involved and dedicated to the idea did the people of Ephrata become that the town and its environs became known as "the dam university."

At last an actual start had been made. Then followed the major task of clearing the site in order to reach the foundation rock. But obstacles were still to arise. Original plans for the dam were for a height of 350 feet above the level of the river. This height, its level today, is enough to allow pumping of water for irrigation and low enough to prevent the water from backing into Canada. Over the years of planning, this height was considered the most feasible.

President Franklin D. Roosevelt, in an attempt to save money, suggested building a low dam for the present, possibly adding more height at a later time. But the low dam idea, while capable of generating electricity, would give the basin no water. The people who had worked and planned for irrigation were disappointed and distressed. Nevertheless, on July 13, 1934, a contract for the low dam was awarded to a merging firm of several different companies.

Four days later, work was begun on thirty-two miles of railroad from a line near Coulee City to the dam site, to haul materials and equipment. During the year it took to build the railroad, the state highway department constructed roads and bridges in the general area.

At last there was cause for rejoicing among the proponents of the irrigation plan. The construction of the high dam was approved and a new contract let. It was almost a year since the low dam contract had been signed.


BUILDING THE DAM

The work of the dam proceeded in steps. The river flow had to be shifted back and forth in its channel so that work could continue. A cofferdam was built to divert and channel the water along the east bank while work got under way on the west bank on the first section of the dam. Sixty acres were enclosed by the cofferdam. These were then excavated, cleaned, and grouted to bedrock to make a firm foundation for the dam. Then the concrete was poured to above the low water level. When the west portion of the dam had been built, the cofferdam was opened to allow the water to pass through to that side. The procedure was then reversed, with building taking place across the river on the east bank.

Many problems were encountered by the workmen. On one occasion, on the east bank, the wet clay slipped down faster than it could be removed. Neither retaining walls nor other methods would stop the sliding mass. Finally, a refrigeration plant was built, and miles of ammonia pipes were buried in the toe of the slide. The clay became an icy dam, and work continued.

At one point in the construction, a record was set when 41,900 tons of concrete were poured in twenty-four hours.

The Grand Coulee Dam is a solid mass of concrete, but it was built in sections of interlocking columns. These columns varied in size from twenty-five by forty-four feet to fifty feet on each side, and were built up five feet at a time. They had to be poured at seventy-two-hour intervals.

Concrete shrinks as it cools. Grout or liquid concrete could not be poured into the joints between the columns until each individual column had cooled. Under normal conditions this would take several hundred years. So pipes were inlaid in the concrete as it was poured and water from the river pumped through them. In this manner, the cooling took some months, after which the grout was finally poured into the joints and the pipes. Buried in the dam today are 1700 miles of this pipe—now part of the construction.

At the outbreak in Europe of World War II, while the dam was nearing completion, the United States was busily building weapons for the countries soon to become its allies, as well as for its own defense. Electrical power became of prime importance, and attention was focused on the Grand Coulee Dam. More and more generators were added. In October, 1941, the first of the 108,000 kilowatt generators began producing. Each weighs 1000 tons.

After the war, industry in the northwest continued and expanded. The demand for power increased. By September, 1951, the last of eighteen such 108,000 kilowatt generators began producing power. Together with three station service generators of 10,000 kilowatts each, the powerplant of the Grand Coulee now has a total installed capacity of nearly two million kilowatts. Eighteen 500 ton turbines of 160,000 horsepower each, and three station service turbines each powered with 14,000 horsepower help make up the present powerplant—the largest in the western hemisphere.

During one one-hour run in October, 1953, the Grand Coulee powerplant had an output of 2,324,000 kilowatts. Marketing agency for the sale of its electricity is the Bonneville Power Administration.

When World War II had ended, it was possible to turn attention to the prime purpose for which the dam was built—irrigation.

While work was started on the pumping plant, the Columbia Basin Project was alive with the building of tunnels, siphons, and storage dams.

Land was classified, soil analyzed and tested. Topographic maps were drawn for each square mile of the area which had been laid out in farms and irrigation blocks. Irrigable and non-irrigable lands were analyzed.

Completion of the waterways system was nearing and the thirsty land lay waiting. Finally, on August 10, 1951, the first water flowed into the main canal. It came from Banks Lake, situated about half way between the dam and Coulee City. The dream is being realized slowly and steadily today as the water reaches more and more of the land each year.

Thousands of miles of waterways aid in the distribution of the irrigation water. From its starting point at the Franklin D. Roosevelt Lake, the giant reservoir behind the Grand Coulee Dam, this system reaches west and south to the town of Pasco, 160 miles away.

Along the way, 2000 miles of canals, including 16 large canal siphons and two tunnels, carry the water of the Columbia River across the coulees and over high ground. En route, various lakes with their earth-fill dams serve as reservoirs, holding the water to be stored or used as seasonal demands for irrigation warrant.

Six pumps, with motors of 65,000 horsepower each, lift the waters of the lake behind the dam over the canyon's rim, a height of 280 feet, sending it on its way south to the lands to be irrigated.

Each pump can raise the water at the rate of 720,000 gallons a minute. One estimate states these six pumps could provide enough water in three minutes to fill one glass of water for every individual in the United States.

A total of twelve pumps is projected for eventual supply of further irrigation in the future. Two are scheduled to begin operating in 1971, two in 1980, and the remaining two by 1986. Officials of the Columbia Basin Project say these additions will be pump-generators, able to pump water into Banks Lake, 1.6 miles away, as well as "to generate electricity for peaking purposes with the use of water brought back down the tubes from Banks Lake."

Carrying the water supplied by the pumps at present, are enormous pipes, twelve feet in diameter. They transport the waters from Lake Roosevelt through the Feeder Canal south to Banks Lake, a twenty-seven-mile-long reservoir, with earth-fill dams at both north and south ends. From here begins the journey to the land to be irrigated, some sixty miles south of the Grand Coulee Dam and embracing an area 100 miles long and sixty miles wide.

What of the dam structure itself? At its crest, it is 4173 feet long and has risen from its bedrock 550 feet. Across the top runs a roadway thirty feet wide, open to vehicles and pedestrians.

Control rooms and a tunnel are below. The tunnel seems weirdly quiet, despite the surge of millions of gallons of water spilling over the top of the dam and the sense of masses of pent-up water. The tunnel appears to stretch endlessly.

In the 800-foot powerhouses at each end of the spillway are housed turbines and generators, the pulsing heart of the dam.

Careful control of each 108,000 kilowatt capacity generator is carried out by a fully installed and functioning computer system which monitors and records data at the dam, watching over generators, switchyards, and the 65,000 horsepower pumps. It is estimated the computer now saves more than $600,000 a year.

As the project grows to accommodate the third powerplant, the operation of the computer will be expanded with it.

The spectacular spillway is 1650 feet wide. At peak summer months, 135 million gallons of water per minute pour over the face of the dam. This sixteen acres of falling water rushes through eleven drum gates and plunges downward to become a giant waterfall.

And so the land where once it was said "even jackrabbits carried a canteen to cross the Columbia Basin," has been transformed, and the desert has been made to bloom. Water and electrical power abound. Agriculture and industry prosper, and the lakes and surrounding countryside provide recreation for the thousands who have flocked to the Columbia River Basin.

# XIV

## THE NETHERLANDS
## RECLAMATION PROJECTS

## LAND WON FROM THE SEA

Green are the fields and fertile; man and herd
Live in contentment on the new-won earth.
Homes nestle by the guarding mound we see
Erected by a people's industry.
A paradise-like land within
Though the sea outside still seeks to win . . .
For freedom, like life, is earned by men
Who each day conquer it again.

J. W. GOETHE, *Faust,* PART II
translated by H. Arthur Klein

Great structures take many forms: they include huge tombs, impressive places of worship and ritual, tall towers, imposing domes and arches, walls seemingly without end, bridges of amazing span, dams of great strength, and waterways of bold design. All these and many other extensive and complex constructions have been built by men to improve or ennoble the lands they live in.

One modern nation, and only one, exists because its people, in an epic struggle of a thousand years and more, have constructed the land itself on which they live and labor. This nation is the Netherlands, often called Holland. The people are the Netherlanders, often called the Dutch. The history of this people is a record of repeated, stubborn struggles, both political and physical. Politically, they resisted foreign rulers and invaders, attaining and holding their independence in the face of heavy odds.

Physically, they fought the devouring tides and storms of the sea. They learned to find, to defend, and finally to extend the land on which they lived. More than any other people, the Dutch made their own soil. That struggle, century after century, shaped the people. The land, and the inhabitants who had won it from the waters—these factors interacted. The Netherlands today, at least the western and most important parts of the nation, may be called the greatest and most extensive man-made structure on earth.

The centuries of toil and increasing technical skill that went into the making and protecting of this crowded, compact, and productive country can be considered as one long building project. As such, it overshadows any other single, integrated effort to oppose and overcome hostile natural forces.

The map tells much of the story, but by no means all. We see a small country. From north to south it measures no more than 190 miles, from east to west not more than 125 miles. It is interwoven with water—inlets and outlets to the sea, lakes, great rivers bearing the run-off waters and the alluvial deposits of large areas of Europe beyond the borders of the Netherlands.

This little land is more densely populated than any other part of Europe. Some thirteen million people today live here on land reclaimed from the sea. And the population is growing swiftly.

The struggle to retain, sustain, and extend these water-menaced acres is literally a matter of defense against disaster—of life against death. Most Netherlanders live and labor at or below the levels reached by the sea at high tide. Floods would sweep them away but for the mighty dikes, stretching miles upon miles. These dikes line the margins of the sea, the banks of canals, and the perimeters of bodies of land that are to be drained, dried out, and cultivated.

Dikes, but for their names, are closely related to the levees built in the United States along the banks of the Mississippi and other rivers that would otherwise wreak havoc with their floods. Dutch dikes built to defend against the North Sea are enormous mounds, 300 or 400 feet wide at the base, thirty or forty feet wide on top. They are high enough to keep out storm waves even at maximum tide. The Netherlands today are protected by nearly 2000 miles of such major sea dikes.

Even more extensive are the dikes along river and canal banks, and around the bodies of "made" land called *polders,* that were once sea-bottom or lake-bottom. These dikes are usually less massive than the sea walls, for they are not battered by the surges and tides of the rampant ocean shore.

Dikes of every kind have been built and repeatedly rebuilt in the Netherlands since the days of the Roman occupation, some 2000 years ago. These dams, designed to defend land from water, have made possible the strange spectacle of a nation's richest, busiest, and most important areas lying below sea level and in constant threat of flooding—if these defenses do not hold.

How many miles of dikes have been built and rebuilt? Dikes,

like the tissues of the human body, are constantly being repaired, rebuilt, replaced. It used to be estimated that a typical dike was completely changed every five or six years. The total distance of Dutch dike building during the past two thousand years might, at this rate, exceed many hundreds of thousands of miles.

"Water, water everywhere. If you like the water you'll love Holland," declares an attractive travel advertisement. The little land has 1000 lakes—and 2000 miles of canals! Its largest city, Amsterdam, likes to boast that not only is it the "Venice of the north," but that it has double the canal mileage of the Italian city famed for its gondolas and glassware.

Hollanders like the water, even love it, but have a healthy respect and fear, too, for what water can do when out of control. The sea and the rivers, and the lakes and the estuaries that interlock with both, have made Holland what it is today. Or, rather, the Hollanders have so molded and managed these waterways that the result is the amazing Netherlands.

To the Dutch, water has been and still is both friend and foe. This becomes clear from the map, from records of a rich and complex history, and from the annals of enormous engineering undertakings, beyond anything comparable elsewhere on earth.

## EARLY SEA CHALLENGERS

Sophisticated Romans, like Pliny, who visited the western Netherlands in the first century of this era, could hardly understand why or how these stubborn barbarians survived. What a miserable life!

Their low-lying land flooded twice daily by the sea, they were forced to place their hovels on mounds, or *terps,* that they heaped up themselves. Some of these man-made hills were almost a quarter of a square mile in area, and 25 feet or more above the surrounding lowlands.

These stubborn ancestors of the stubborn Dutch were no newcomers even in Pliny's day. Their ancestors, too, had somehow hung on in this battleground between the North Sea tides, the wild winds, the erratic rivers, and the shifting sand dunes. They managed to eke out existences as fishermen, herdsmen, or farmers. Floods ravaged their lands, swept away their possessions, and drowned many of them—but always they doggedly returned, rebuilt, and restarted the battle with the low-lying lands and the treacherous waters.

The Romans undertook to build various dike defenses against river flooding, including a great dike system all along one side of the Rhine to where it reached the sea in the land of shifting sand dunes.

The Dutch adopted the dike method, began to connect one terps-mound with another by means of such sea walls, and within a relatively few centuries had begun to form chainlike rings whose links were terps and dikes.

Within such a protected ring, water could be drained and the newly exposed land, once the sea-salt had been extracted or leached away, provided fertile soil for farming. Such a dike-guarded ring around new soil came to be called a *polder,* a word of prime importance in the battle of Dutchmen against the sea and streams.

Polders were linked with polders by additional dikes. Thus the available land grew, link by link, dike by dike, polder by polder. But always such growth was punctuated by catastrophic floods that swept away gains and oftentimes drowned vast numbers of people and livestock.

From the Middle Ages until modern times, the Netherlands has sustained major floods on the average of every six or seven years. These floods often were not created solely by the wind-whipped waves and high tides of the North Sea. Commonly they were caused also by river-borne late winter or spring freshets from melting snows in lands to the east and south of the Netherlands.

For, as the map will clearly show, much of the modern Netherlands, and especially its southern provinces, has been formed by the deltas or discharge regions of three great rivers, crossing this country in an east to west direction on their way to the sea. Most northerly flows the Rhine, which splits into two streams, the lower Rhine and the Waal, as it crosses the Netherlands. Next is the Maas, (or Meuse) River. Then, at the extreme southwestern tip of what is now Netherlands territory, appears the mouth of the Scheldt river, which comes up from within Belgium, just south of the Netherlands.

The mouths of these three rivers form a complex delta region, with many estuaries, islands, swampy areas, shifting currents, and tides.

This is the great delta region of the Netherlands. The silt and deposits carried seaward by these rivers have actually supplied rich soil from which the islands and lowlands were formed at the sea's edge.

Every river mouth is both a way *out* for silt-laden fresh water, and a way *in* for salt seawater when the ocean's high tides become strong enough to beat back the river's flow.

When a stormy sea is trying to force its way inland, and swollen rivers are trying to discharge their streams into the sea, the combined high waters can break out of stream beds and sweep over dikes, flooding the country roundabout and causing vast damage.

Such catastrophes took place again and again during the centuries.

In 839 C.E., vast floods threw the river system into chaos.

In mid-December, 1287, a major flood took the lives of some 50,000 people.

In 1300, during equinoctial storms, the North Sea tore its way through the barrier separating it from the inland Lake Flevo. This cataclysm swept away hundreds of villages and created the Zuider Zee (Southern Sea). It caused the salt waters, the damaging surges, and the tides of the North Sea to hammer at the very heart of the Netherlands.

In 1421, the river Maas ruptured its dike and rushed into the polders of Bresbach, drowning 10,000 people.

And so it went on, reconstruction and extension alternating with catastrophic combinations of winds, tides, and river flow. The Netherlanders learned how to build bigger, tougher, more resistant dikes. They ringed the new Zuider Zee with dikes so stout that they held it within its new limits until modern times.

They learned too to fight the ravages of sea and wind with new weapons. The shifting sand dunes along the North Sea coast they managed to anchor down by means of a particularly tough-rooted grass called *helm*. The fine-reaching roots formed a mat that held the sand.

They learned to weave their own mats of willows or reeds as anchorage for the foundation of the ever-increasing dikes along sea-coast, riverbanks, and canal margins. Stone was scarce in the Netherlands, but as far as possible they made do with gravel, pebbles, and clay, firmly compacted, and vigilantly tended.

The story of the Dutch boy who saved the nation by plugging up the leaky dike with his finger cannot be true—though often repeated. Yet it contains a great truth of Netherlands history: only vigilance and dogged, devoted effort by millions of ordinary hard-working Dutchmen made possible the persistence of this people on their hard-won land.

New giants were enlisted to aid them, beginning their work in the fifteenth century—four-armed giants, dotting the level landscapes—the windmills. Some people assume that these picturesque landmarks were kept busy grinding wheat for flour or other grains for fine Dutch beer. Mostly, however, they were driving great pumps, sucking the moisture out of drainage canals, pushing it out, beyond the dikes, into the canals and into the sea where it belonged.

The flat, low land was constantly swept by great gales from the North Sea. The windmills converted them into mechanical power for pumping water, hour after hour, day after day. Lakes were drained in this way by wind-power, and the fertile lake bottoms became farmland and meadowland where cows grazed and gave rich milk.

The increases in farmable, grazeable lands were large. During the first half of the sixteenth century, some 80,000 acres were gained, or recovered in this way. During the first half of the seventeenth century—130,000 acres.

William the Silent (1533–1584), one of the great heroes of Dutch resistance against the tyranny of Spain, was aware, also, of his people's needs in their struggles against the forces of nature. His dike-master for the sea and river fronts was the talented engineer, Andries Vierlingh. An equally eminent master of inland drainage was Jan Leeghwater.

Vierlingh urged collective action on a large scale by means of a governmental authority with powers to defend the community against coastal dangers. Leeghwater, after directing many major reclamation projects carried out with the aid of windmills, proposed in 1617 the drainage of the great Sea of Haarlem itself. He was laughed at. Yet, in the middle of the nineteenth century it was done —with the help of steam pumps!

## A POEM AND THE POLDERS

A great poet and playwright in nearby England set down some haunting lines during the early 1590s. William Shakespeare's *Sonnet* Number 64 used a comparison quite familiar to the Netherlanders, England's near neighbors across the North Sea. He wrote:

> When I have seen the hungry ocean gain
> Advantage on the kingdom of the shore,
> And the firm soil win of the wat'ry main,
> Increasing store with loss and loss with store;
> When I have seen such interchange of state,
> Or state itself confounded to decay;
> > Ruin hath taught me thus to ruminate,
> > That time will come and take my love away.

The Dutch were by no means disposed to stand by brooding, while time or the hungry ocean took away the land they loved and depended on for life.

They continued to counterattack, using more effective tools and techniques. During the centuries since the Renaissance and Reformation eras, they gained not only fertile acres but priceless experience and skills, all at the cost of heroic labors.

Specialists in dike and polder work were trained from youth onward. Most of these *polderjongens,* polder lads, came from the delta region in the south. Their particular homeland is Sliedrecht, a little west of Rotterdam in the South Holland province.

Some of the Netherlands' greatest builders have praised these booted, stolid, slow, and stubborn tamers of the hungry ocean's surges. In the sixteenth century, dikemaster Vierlingh paid tribute to them; and nearly four hundred years later, in the present century, the eminent reclamation engineer, Dr. J. van Veen, spoke his admiration for these indispensable workers.

He cited their skills with the heavy woven willow mattresses by which they anchor the dikes, and their uncanny ability to direct the unwieldy dredging machines. Strange heroes, perhaps, yet they "have journeyed over the entire world to do their mud and mattress work." They have demonstrated in their own little land and elsewhere, too, that they know how to "choke off wild streams."

The engineers, overseers, and *polderjongens* gained new advantages as advances in science and technology improved their tools. Development of the steam engine by the early nineteenth century did away with former dependence on the muscle power of humans or animals, or on devices driven by the wind.

One of the sights visitors to the Netherlands are advised to see is the one-time steam pumping station at Cruquius, now a national museum of land reclamation and polderizing. Here, preserved in gratitude and glory, is a steam pump that helped drain the Sea of Haarlem, pouring out 85,000 gallons of water each minute during more than eighty years. When it was retired from use in 1933, it was preserved for posterity to view with respect.

At the polder of the Wieringer Sea, finished in 1930, one pumping station has a capacity of 330,000 gallons a minute. Such are the drainage needs of this project of 50,000 acres area, much of it eighteen feet under sea level!

Beside steam power, the last century brought the flexible and convenient electric motor. Later came the gasoline and diesel engines and with them new and more powerful vehicles for travel on both land and water.

Improved transportation made heavier, harder, and more suitable building materials available for the dikes and polder structures, such as stone quarried outside the little Netherlands.

The nineteenth century was an era of enormous activity in winning land from the waters. About 124,000 acres of polders were diked around, drained, and brought into cultivation. Many thousands of these acres stood ten, twelve, fourteen feet or more below sea level.

Science made discoveries too that brought cause for alarm, rather than confidence. The continual cycles of diking up, draining, and drying out land that had been below water resulted in soil shrinkage. A general lowering of land level became apparent from this and other causes. It is estimated that since 1000 C.E., an average land subsidence or lowering of between seven and one-half to ten feet has taken place in these vital western areas of the Netherlands. The Lowlands were sinking even lower!

This was part of the cost of the great struggle against the natural environment. It meant greater difficulties and dangers in defending the hard-won land against future storms and floods.

Warnings continued to strike from time to time—some of them very costly. In 1836, a great flood almost engulfed the cities of Amsterdam, Haarlem, and Leyden. Then, in 1916, during World War I, in which the Netherlands remained neutral, the Zuider Zee was whipped over its banks and catastrophic floods took their toll again.

This finally forced action along the lines of a bold plan that had been proposed years before by a Dutch engineer and government official named Cornelis Lelys. Actual construction took place, following the war, during the years 1923–1932. In this period was completed the greatest dike of all—a twenty-mile dam running straight across the mouth of what had been the Zuider Zee. This imposing barrier, called an enclosing dam, runs from the northernmost tip of the province of North Holland, in a northwesterly direction, to the shore of the province of Friesland.

The famous old Zuider Zee is now no more. Its place is taken by the Ijssel-Meer, a lake, filled with fresh water from inflowing streams. This has several vast advantages. For one the over-salting of Dutch soil is retarded. The infiltration of salt seawater from the Zuider Zee had been harming agriculture in the regions around its edges. Another gain is the fact that the Ijssel Lake is now a tideless body of water, protected against the batterings of the North Sea. The land around this lake will be less eroded and should sink less than that around the old Zuider Zee. Finally, in four great polder areas the former sea is being converted into arable land. When this phase of the work is finished, well over one-half million acres will have been added to the limited land area of Holland. There will still remain a lovely freshwater lake of about a quarter of a million acres, but it will be surrounded by five large new and productive polders, each with its own protective dikes and drainage canals, each with its own population of farmers, dairymen, and workers.

In succession the steps of diking, draining, and readying for occupancy have been applied to these great additions, all within a single integrated project:

| | | |
|---|---|---|
| THE WIERINGERMEER POLDER (completed in 1931) | 50,000 | acres |
| NORTH-EAST POLDER ( " " 1943) | 120,000 | " |
| EAST FLEVOLAND (drained in 1956–1957) | 135,000 | " |
| MARKERWARD | 140,000 | " |
| SOUTH FLEVOLAND | 112,000 | " |

The Netherlands previously had a total of only about eight million acres. Of these, about six and one-quarter million were used for agriculture. The Zuider Zee polder additions, when completed, will represent a seven percent increase in total land area, and a nine percent increase in farm land. These are great gains in a land so small and so densely populated.

By the time the new areas are fully populated and in production, they will contain from 100,000 to 150,000 residents, and the last four of them together will form a new province, the twelfth in the nation. The capital city of the province, fittingly, is Lelystad or Lelys City.

These newly made lands offer something that travelers can find nowhere else. Everything about them has been deliberately decided and planned in advance—the placement of roads and villages, the subdivision into farms, recreation areas and school grounds, church sites, and shopping areas.

Human purpose and planning have seldom held sway so completely over all the factors that shape a region or a locality. A host of complex problems have been considered and solved by the planning agencies. The selection of farmers and families to move into the new polder areas has been carried on with great care. Applicants have far outnumbered the available new farms.

The planners have not been able to foresee all the changes and conditions that would arise. Policies followed in the development of each new polder have been revised and guided by experiences gained from the earlier ones.

The systematic unfolding of the polder development in the Ijssel-Meer offers special interest to Americans who are concerned about the destruction or spoilage of natural resources in their own country. Pollution of air by smog, of lakes and rivers by harmful chemicals, destruction of natural beauties and wilderness areas—all these represent losses to the citizens of those areas and the nation as a whole.

The structure of the Zuider Zee project in the Netherlands, however, is such as to assure advantages, rather than losses, to the citizens of the nation as a whole, as well as to those relatively few who are becoming permanent residents of the newly created lands.

## FROM NORTH TO SOUTH, AND SOUTH TO NORTH

The name of the famous, and now vanished, *Zuider Zee* meant Southern Sea. It reminded the Netherlanders, during more than six centuries, how far south into their little land the raging North Sea had forced its way.

Now, on the site of part of that former sea lies the lovely new Ijssel Lake. Its fresh water supply constantly demonstrates how the streams and inlets interlock all over this little land, from south to north, as well as from east to west. Ijssel Lake is, in fact, fed by the Ijssel River, a relatively small branching-off of the mighty Rhine, a stream of 850 miles length. The Rhine rises in Switzerland, then becomes in succession boundaries between that nation and Austria; between Switzerland and Germany; between Germany and France. Then the Rhine flows northerly through Germany, swings westward, and enters the Netherlands through the eastern province of Gelderland.

Just after this entry, the Rhine splits into two branches: the southern branch is called the Waal, the northern branch is known as the Lower Rhine. Both these rivers flow eastward across the Netherlands, but the Lower Rhine, which carries only about half as much water as the Waal, soon sends north another stream, the Ijssel. This flows finally into what was once the salty Zuider Zee, but is now the freshwater Ijssel Lake. Between ten and twelve percent of the total flow of the Rhine passes thus through the Ijssel to provide the precious fresh-water supply for Ijssel Lake.

There is another stream with a similar name—the Hollandsche Ijssel, or Ijsel. It flows near the great port city of Rotterdam in the province of South Holland. Names, as well as the interrelationships, of Dutch streams, estuaries, and waterways are often confusing to outsiders. The fact that *ijs* or *ijzel* means "ice" in Dutch may suggest the origin of these river names and the state of their waters in winter.

All but a small fraction of the mighty water volume of the Rhine thus moves westward across the Netherlands, a land that was to a large extent born as the delta or alluvial deposit of that river. To Rhine waters are added also the waters and the silt-content of the Maas River. It rises in France, where it is called the Meuse, and crosses Belgium, where it is joined by the Sambre River. Then, entering the Netherlands, it flows into the Waal channel of the Rhine.

Still further south flows the Scheldt River, which, though Belgian in origin, enters the Dutch delta province of Zeeland shortly after it flows past the great Belgian harbor of Antwerp.

Thus the Dutch delta interweaves and combines the seaward flows of the three potent streams: the Rhine, the Maas, and the Scheldt. The surges and tides of the sea resist and often overcome these river currents.

Even on maps, the uneasy, chaotic nature of these incessant watery conflicts can be glimpsed. Those fortunate enough to cruise by ship or boat through this area come to understand even more clearly how manifold and complex are its currents, its difficulties, and its dangers.

As the great streams approach the open sea, their waters divide, subdivide, and recombine in intricate patterns. They pass among the islands and estuaries that have been formed by their endless interactions with the ocean's tides. Even a large, detailed modern map scarcely does justice to the complexities of this great area where sea, soil, and streams have engaged in so many centuries of inter-action and conflict.

Generally, as in other great delta areas, the river waters fan out-ward through many mouths to reach the open sea. Each river mouth is also an open door through which high tides of the sea can surge inland, salting the soil along the stream banks, and often flooding the lowlands destructively.

When these sea surges advance inland, they converge and con-centrate. What is a fanning-out for the outflow of rivers, becomes a drawing together and a compounding of the inflowing high tides from the sea. Thus the delta results in added dangers for all the land lying about its banks.

Again and again through the centuries, great catastrophes, com-bining sea tides, storms, and high river run-offs, have ravaged this rich delta region of the southwestern Netherlands.

For a time some Netherlanders assumed—largely because they hoped—that the great conversion of the old Zuider Zee would bring relative security to their land. Leading Dutch water-engineers warned otherwise, and thanks to their abundant rich background of experience and study they are the world's outstanding specialists in their field.

## WORLD WAR II STRIKES THE NETHERLANDS

Action to control the dangers of the Delta region might have been launched long ago, but for the ravages of the German occupation of the Netherlands during World War II. Between the years 1940–1945, the Netherlands suffered enormous destruction hun-ger, and oppression. As the invasion began, the German air force, at the direction of the Nazi dictators, Hitler and Goering, blasted the heart of Rotterdam to ruins in a murderous attack without mili-tary justification. Then followed the long and bitter years of occu-pation.

The final expulsion of the forces flying the Swastika flag came only when the war in Europe was at its close in May, 1945. The withdrawing Germans stole from the Netherlands all they could carry, stripping Holland of nearly 30,000 machines and between 85 and 90 industrial installations. About forty percent of industrial production was lost. More than 90,000 houses were destroyed.

Floods inundated more than 225,000 acres. Gas and electric production were down to less than a fifth of their 1938 levels. Usable railway lines were reduced by forty percent. Agricultural yields were off by more than half. In the southern provinces, including the delta and adjacent regions, industrial production was down to almost nothing.

The Dutch struggle to restart their economy and recover from the ravages of the Nazi occupation was stubborn, resourceful, and, eventually, successful. A major sign of the Netherlands recovery was the return to active planning for protection of the endangered delta region. A group of experts completed and submitted a detailed plan at the beginning of 1953. It included the warning that an especially heavy storm might shatter the barriers then protecting this vital region.

Within days afterward, as if to demonstrate that the unlikely can always become the actual, a fierce northwest storm began whipping the sea waters toward the coastal gaps. High tides were also on their way, adding to the battering force of the waves. At the same time— for it was early February—the Rhine, Maas, and Scheldt rivers were sending seaward swollen waters fed by melting snows in the Swiss and French mountains.

These combined forces struck and passed over the dikes. Now floods battered the great barriers from the land side as well as the water side. By the second high tide, the dikes had begun to breach, and the damage ran rampant.

The final toll in the ghastly catastrophe included loss of more than 1800 lives, 133 villages and towns overwhelmed, 47,000 houses destroyed, and 375,000 acres of land flooded.

Damage in dollars was over a milliard, as the Dutch would say— or a billion, as Americans call it. Several hundred miles of ruined dikes awaited rebuilding.

The Dutch nation was appalled and aroused. Great as the damage had been, it had come close to being vastly greater still. Only by the most strenuous effort had it been possible to hold the dikes that guarded the major centers of the Netherlands. Had they gone, as they so nearly did, Amsterdam, Rotterdam, and much of the Hague would have been submerged. Loss of life would have been tremendous. It has been said quite soberly that such a catastrophe might have meant the end of the Netherlands as a functioning nation.

## THE DELTA DESIGN GOES INTO ACTION

The terrible disaster swept away the last hesitations and reservations. Action followed swiftly. Before the end of the month, a committee was appointed and the Delta Design moved from paper toward reality. A schedule of dates for completing its major constructions was set up. Between 1960 and the last of the 1970s, four stupendous super-dikes or dams were to be built in the open sea, sealing off the great Delta outlets.

The diagram shows their location by numbers. First to be completed was the dam, about 3000 feet wide, across the Veersche Gat (4). Next, scheduled to be finished not long after these lines are written, is the dam across the Haringvliet (1), three miles long, with gigantic sluice-gates to permit winter and springtime ice and overflow water to reach the sea in safety.

By the beginning of 1970, another great dam is due to be finished, sealing off the Brouwershavensche Gat (2). And finally, the giant of them all—a five-mile dam to seal the mouth of the Ooster Schelde (3).

These barriers, confronting the open sea, became possible to build only with the aid of preliminary barriers to be built first, further inland, along the communicating estuaries and channels.

One of these was a protective seal that could be swung into place across the mouth of the Hollandsche Ijssel (10), the river mentioned earlier, just east of Rotterdam.

The other inner preliminary barriers, listed from north to south, are those shown on our map at the locations numbered 9, 8, and 7.

With a total of eight barriers of varied size and type, three extra-

ordinary results will be attained, each one essential to the defense, the well-being, and the future progress of the delta region as well as of the nation as a whole.

First, the artificial channel called the New Waterway (5) remains open, as it must, permitting shipping to move between the major port of Rotterdam and the open sea. Now, however, this channel becomes the main run-off outlet for the waters of the Rhine and Maas rivers. The force of this flow will be sufficient to prevent the salt tidal surges of the sea from forcing their way inland, salinating and damaging the land around and behind Rotterdam.

The dikes alongside this important channel are raised higher, because of the greater volumes of water that it must convey.

Second, at the extreme south of this system lies the Westerschelde estuary (6). It too remains open to the sea, as it must, to permit shipping to pass freely to and from the Belgian port of Antwerp. This channel can neither take from nor give water to the waterways that lie north of it. It is thus safely isolated.

Third, the entire network of channels and waterways lying between the Nieuwe Waterweg to the north and the Westerschelde to the south, will be sealed off from the sea. This becomes, then, a tide-free, surge-free, protected and controlled fresh-water lake system. See 11, 1, 2, 3, and 4.

A variety of sluice gates and special run-off arrangements are provided to permit regulation of levels within this complex system. It is to be operated in coordination, with full use of information as to levels and conditions in all its many parts.

Electrical and hydraulic controls will move mighty gates, locks, and pumping equipment. It will be, when fully completed and operative about 1980, the most audacious, most elaborate, and at the same time the cleverest combination of constructions that men have ever assembled in their age-old effort to make the flowing and surging waters of the earth work for them, and not against them.

Totally new and sensational methods of construction have been devised in preparing for and building the great dams across these large inlets to the open sea. We cannot here describe them all in detail. However, they can be summed up by saying that most of this

great complex of construction will be accomplished by techniques never before used, except in miniature form, prior to the launching of this Delta Design. It is both bold and novel.

Two extraordinary methods stand out in particular. One is the use of floating boxes or caissons to solve the problems of erecting dams across channels beset by surges and currents. It is an application of the old device of scuttling a ship to block up a harbor inlet.

Here, the Dutch have designed great ready-made concrete boxes with sliding doors that can be opened or closed. With their doors closed these caisson boxes float and can be towed into position over prepared foundations. Then, when their doors are opened, they sink into position and remain set, while the tides surge back and forth through their openings.

When the full line-up of caissons is side by side in position, at an appropriate time, all their doors are dropped shut at once, and the sea is locked out, while on the other side of the completed dam lies tide-free water.

More than half a dozen huge caisson boxes were thus closed to complete the barrier across the Veersche Gat (4) in the early 1960s.

The next largest barrier, and the next to approach completion, was the dam to block the Haringvliet seamouth (1). Its plans called for a total length of about 16,000 feet, of which more than 3000 feet would be occupied by giant sluice gates. These were included in order to let through the annual visitations of inrushing ice and high water that might otherwise prove disastrous.

Such sluice gates had to be built on dry land. This meant constructing an island in mid-channel. To do this, a cofferdam was first built. It was a dam or dike in oval form, whose inside could be pumped dry to form the temporary island. Thus was born the greatest cofferdam in the history of man's constructions on earth. Its inside area totals about 1,800,000 square feet.

Within this water-free sanctuary, building of the heavy sluice-gate structures could go on with relative ease. Permanent dam walls were constructed, first on the seaward side of the cofferdam, and then on the side away from the sea.

The foundations for the huge sluice gates were anchored to the bottom by more than 20,000 pilings made of concrete, not of wood. For each such piling, more than a ton of steel was incorporated in the total underpinnings for the sluice gates.

At the same time, work was not neglected on the sections of the dam that are not to have sluice gates on top. For these a score of caissons were floated into position, sunk, and secured to the bottom.

The completed giant dam will bear at its crest a broad automobile highway. This same road will run also atop the great barrier structures that seal off the next three sea-mouths to the south: the Brouwershavensche Gat (2), the Ooster Schelde (3), and the Veersche Gat (4).

This highway will form an integral part of the network of high-speed roads that bring every part of the Netherlands within rapid reach of the rest. Beside carrying motorists between such points as Walcheren and Bergen op Zoom, it will beyond doubt bring many visitors to gaze in awe and admiration at these giant works of man that are taming the tides.

Other advanced techniques have been developed during the course of construction of the Delta Design. Though the Netherlands is a tiny nation, even with all its additions of polderized and protected land raised from the sea bottom, its contributions have been enormous in the fields of man's mastery of hydraulics and marine construction.

## THE UNENDING STRUGGLE CONTINUES

Even with the completion of all present plans for the Ijssel Lake and the Delta Design, the struggle of Dutchmen against the sea will not be ended. It will merely have reached a new level of advantage to humans.

In their history, the Dutch have found the sea to be both foe and friend. It has sought to swamp and steal their land. Yet it has also given them the riches of its fisheries, and the benefits of shipping that made them the carriers for much of the rest of the world.

Water is an essential and indispensable part of the world of men, women, and children of the Netherlands. The organized, careful, yet bold efforts of their leaders has been directed toward eliminating the sea's ability to cause harm, while securing for themselves and, above all, for their posterity, its many productive and pleasant aspects.

Not only has the great construction of the people of the Netherlands been the winning of their land from the waters, but the discovery of new ways in which to make better and safer the lives of those who live there. The making of their land has helped to form them as a nation and a people noted for persistence, patience, and pride in what they have won.

# XV

## THE UNITED NATIONS BUILDINGS

## STAFF HEADQUARTERS FOR PEACE

We the peoples of the United Nations
determined to save succeeding generations
from the scourge of war which twice within
our lifetime has brought untold sorrow to
mankind . . . have resolved to combine our
efforts to accomplish these aims.

—Preamble to the UN Charter

"It is a kind of war, and I suppose I am the commander in chief," mused a gentle man, whose dignified, somewhat sad face suggests the scholar and philosopher, rather than the military man.

Then U Thant, Secretary-General of the United Nations, continued, "The staff headquarters is the United Nations Building here in New York, and that is where the general staff operates.

"But the real battle is not there. It is out in the front lines in every country in every continent where the United Nations flag flies. That is where the real fighting goes on, only we are fighting not against mankind, but *for* mankind. . . . That is what the war is."

On the eastern edge of the crowded island of Manhattan beside the East River, in his office near the top of the great UN staff headquarters building, U Thant, that modest man from Burma, spoke as the chief civil servant of the most truly international organization that this troubled world has yet evolved.

Among the world's greatly significant structures, none today exceeds in importance these headquarters of the continuing war for mankind—a war whose outcome remains so desperately in doubt that many question not only the success of the UN, but even the survival of the world whose last and best hope it represents.

Here is the home office, the meeting place, and also the symbol of the world forces organized to seek survival. It stands in an era of nuclear weapons, supersonic bombers, napalm, and bacteriochemical methods of mass killing. It is an era whose alternatives for the future have been rapidly narrowed to two and no more: one world —or none.

In a sense, these UN headquarters were conceived to accomplish the reverse of what happened in the myth of the Tower of Babel. That mythical construction was the occasion for the origin of misunderstanding, language barriers, conflicts, and confusion among men. This construction is designed to assure constant communication, comprehension, cooperation, and protected peace.

These headquarters are still relatively new, though the needs they serve are old in the world's bloody history. The UN itself was launched only in 1945, at the conclusion of history's second world war within less than thirty years.

By 1953, big, likable Trygve Lie, the first Secretary-General, was returning to his native Norway. One of the many mementos of his completed term of service was a gold medal given to him by some of his staff. It pictured in relief the famous and contrasting group of buildings beside the East River, and the inscription praised Lie's contributions as "creator of the UN Secretariat, builder of the permanent headquarters, spokesman for peace."

More than 120 nations, old and new, are members of the UN. More will certainly be added, provided that the UN machinery for peace continues to function. The greatness of a structure lies in the minds of its beholders, not in its dimensions or materials. The hopes and concerns of millions of war-weary and peace-seeking people throughout the world are focused on what takes place within and by means of these striking staff headquarters beside the East River.

About a million people a year visit these headquarters just to see them, inside as well as out. To most of them the visit gives a greater sense of understanding the aims and the methods of the UN. New things are being attempted here, in new ways. Admittedly, results thus far achieved lag behind needs. The threat of another and perhaps final war has not been wiped out of the world. Yet the possibilities that remain of avoiding wars and the threats of wars, all involve the machinery for which these structures were created.

The UN buildings could be said to serve as the headquarters for the hopes of the world. This can be better illustrated by a rapid review of their origins, rather than by fine phrases about their aims.

## WORLD WAR I AND THE LEAGUE OF NATIONS

From 1914 to 1918, World War I raged. More than sixty-five million men were mobilized by the warring nations. Total deaths exceeded eight and one-half million. More than twenty-one million were wounded. Other losses, human and material, were too vast to supply meaningful figures.

Out of the peace conferences that followed the defeat of Germany and the other Central powers, emerged the plan for a League of Nations. It had been supported most strongly by President Woodrow Wilson of the United States, yet after the League was launched, the U. S. Senate refused the approval necessary to make this country a member.

All other major eligible powers participated, however, to some extent in the League, except the U.S. and Saudi Arabia. Lacking the United States and otherwise crippled by limitations, the League did not serve to maintain peace for long. It came into existence formally in 1920. In little more than 13 years, by the autumn of 1933, Germany under Hitler withdrew from the League—and by September 1, 1939, the new German war machine went into action against Poland, and World War II began.

The League can be said to have survived, somewhat feebly, from 1920 to 1933, and then to have dragged on an existence in name only for another six or eight years.

Even during the earlier period before it was openly defied, the League had been poorly provided with funds, support and physical means. Its first headquarters was a 200-room former hotel in Geneva, Switzerland, purchased for that purpose.

The League's income from its member nations was meager—little more than five million dollars a year, or a tiny fraction of the expenditures on armaments of any one of its principal member nations.

Finally, a start was made in 1929 on a permanent headquarters to house the League at Geneva. Work proceeded slowly. In 1936, this headquarters called the *Palais des Nations* (Palace of Nations) was completed, in the center of a Europe manifestly being rushed toward another war as rapidly as Hitler and his aides could hurry.

The cold and empty elegance of the *Palais des Nations* soon enough seemed a mockery.

WORLD WAR II

From 1939 to 1945, most of mankind was swept into the second and vastly more destructive World War. Deaths in battle soared to fantastic heights. Such losses have been estimated at 7.5 million for the Soviet Union, 3.5 million for Germany-Austria, 2.2 million for China, 1.2 million for Japan—a total of 14.4 million for these four alone.

Beside battle deaths and numbers of wounded, the war years also brought between six and seven million murders of noncombatants and prisoners in extermination camps equipped with poison gas chambers and furnaces operated by the Germans at many points in their own and occupied territories.

Direct and indirect loss of life in World War II is difficult to estimate, because, to the other fatalities should be added deaths due to malnutrition, disease, and outright starvation resulting from the war.

Never before had civilians and noncombatants suffered to such an extent. Aerial bombings of one great city after another— Warsaw, Rotterdam, London, Berlin, Dresden, and others, were followed after the end of the fighting in Europe by the first atomic bombings that devastated the Japanese cities of Hiroshima and Nagasaki.

In destruction of human life, health, and wealth, World War II almost certainly exceeded by at least six to ten times the destruction wrought in World War I. Clearly, mankind itself could not survive if destructive wars were to recur.

By late summer of 1944, though World War II was still raging in Europe, it had become clear that the German armies were being forced back and victory must come to the powers united against the Swastika emblem. A series of conferences, meeting between August and October, 1944, at Dumbarton Oaks, Washington, D. C., brought together representatives of the United States and the United Kingdom (Great Britain), first with the Soviet Union, and then with China. The subject was how to preserve peace after it was restored.

There was general agreement that a new and effective international organization should be formed.

THE SAN FRANCISCO CONFERENCE
AND THE CHARTER

Victory in Europe had been assured when, in a memorable period of two months, April 25 to June 26, 1945, the United Nations Conference on International Organizations was held in San Francisco, California. Delegations from scores of nations took part. In a mood of elation and anticipation, there was drawn up the great document known as the Charter of the United Nations.

It was signed for fifty nations on the closing day of the historic conference, and before the end of October of that year it went into effect.

The structures that house the United Nations form our principal subject here, rather than the organization of the UN itself. Nevertheless, the Charter remains a document of major importance. It can be comfortably printed in a dozen or more book pages, but its applications and means are world-wide. For millions of people, the UN means mainly the stirring words of its Charter—that, and also the familiar combination of buildings that now form its headquarters.

Like the Constitution of the United States, the UN Charter begins with a preamble that tells the world its aims. Words such as these speak eloquently to men and women who long for an end to wars and the threat of wars, and who seek better lives for themselves and their children:

"We the peoples of the United Nations determined to save succeeding generations from the scourge of war which twice within our lifetime has brought untold sorrow to mankind, and . . .

"To reaffirm faith in fundamental human rights, in the dignity and worth of the human person, in the equal rights of men and women, and of nations large and small, and

"To establish conditions under which justice and respect for obligations arising from treaties and other sources of international law can be maintained, and

"To promote social progress and better standards of life in larger freedom . . . and

"To unite our strength to maintain international peace and security, and

"To insure . . . that armed force shall not be used, save in the common interest, and

"To employ international machinery for the promotion of the economic and social advancement of all peoples, *have resolved to combine our efforts to accomplish these aims."* [Italics added.]

Basically, the nations that signed the Charter promised to keep the peace and to secure it against breach. They also agreed to work together to create conditions—political, economic, and social conditions—that would favor continued peace, rather than conflict. The Charter does not treat peace as something separate and apart from other human affairs. It recognizes that the way people live and think influences them toward peace-keeping, on one hand—or war-making, on the other. The UN, then, was to provide international machinery to strengthen the peace-keeping tendencies and discourage the warlike influences.

At the same time, the Charter clearly barred the new UN organization from interfering in the internal affairs of any nation.

Any clear-cut threat to the peace of the world, any breach of that peace, or any aggressive act against another nation, was not an internal matter. On the contrary, it was an action to be countered by peace-enforcing measures of the UN.

Six principal organs or arms of the UN are established by the Charter: (1) the General Assembly, (2) the Security Council,

(3) the Economic and Social Council, (4) the Trusteeship Council, (5) the International Court of Justice, and (6) the Secretariat.

The Charter tells the tasks that each of these divisions should fulfill. The Secretariat staff is to be headed and chosen by the chief administrative officer, the Secretary-General. The Secretariat, in fact, is a corps of international civil servants who are pledged to serve the purposes and interests of the United Nations, not of any one nation or group of nations.

From the first, the international nature of the UN Secretary-General and his staff was emphasized. The staff was to be chosen so as to secure "the highest standards of efficiency, competence, and integrity" and also to recruit the staff "on as wide a geographic basis as possible." This meant a Secretariat drawn from many nations. A further safeguard was provided by giving the General Assembly power to make the rules under which the Secretary-General could appoint his staff. Each member nation had equal voice in the General Assembly, and could be expected to be alert if staff selection appeared biased against its own interests.


## THE GENERAL ASSEMBLY SELECTS A SITE

In January, 1946, the UN General Assembly met for the first time, in London's solid, old-fashioned Westminster Palace. By February 1, Trygve Lie of Norway had been unanimously chosen first Secretary-General, to serve a five-year term.

Without much loss of time, another fundamental question was settled: where should the UN have its permanent headquarters? The decisive sentiment among the delegations was against using Geneva, seat of the feeble and ill-fated League of Nations—or indeed against the choice of any alternative site in Switzerland or even in Europe.

With notable unanimity, the General Assembly decided the permanent headquarters site should be in the United States. It did not specify, however, in what city or region. High hopes and abundant rumors immediately began to rise in widely scattered American communities. Boston, Philadelphia, and San Francisco all had their champions. Other groups urged the advantages of some suitable suburban area within relatively easy reach of New York City, such as sites in Westchester or Connecticut.

The flurry of proposals and counter-proposals was finally cut short, however, by an unexpected event.

It was revealed December 11, 1946, by Warren R. Austin, then serving as the permanent representative of the United States to the UN. The multimillionaire, John D. Rockefeller, Jr., had offered to contribute $8.5 million to make ready for the UN a piece of land along the East River in Manhattan.

Less than two days after this revelation, the die was cast. The offer was accepted, and preparations were begun to create a home appropriate to the needs and status of the UN.

The site as it stood in late December, 1946, appeared dismal and discouraging. It was a repulsive, dilapidated tangle of slum tenements, run-down factories, warehouses, breweries, slaughterhouses, and unkempt docks. Vision and experience were needed to see, past this sordid congestion, that beauty and splendor could be achieved here.

A vast program of clean-up, area improvement, and long-range landscaping was essential. This was contributed by the City of New York, at a cost estimated at more than twenty-six million dollars. Needless to say, this proved one of the most worthwhile outlays for self-improvement that a city has ever made. The UN headquarters are among the continuing attractions that bring visitors to New York, and pride to the hearts of New Yorkers.

The actual size of the site is not great, except by comparison with the crowded condition of the over-built island of Manhattan.

The total area is about eighteen acres. It extends from Forty-second Street at the south to Forty-eighth Street on the north, and from First Avenue on the west to what is now the Franklin D. Roosevelt Drive along the East River. On the opposite side of the river lies New York's Borough of Queens. A little north—or upstream—stretches the lengthy Welfare Island in the middle of the river, extending from Fiftieth Street to Eighty-sixth Street. About on a line with Fifty-ninth Street, the Queensboro Bridge crosses the East River and Welfare Island.

The next problem was clear, but by no means easy to solve. How best to use this unusual site? After all, it lay on the margin of Manhattan itself, the world's most congested concentration of vertical-upward-construction.

## AN INTERNATIONAL BOARD OF DESIGN

To supply solutions, the UN fittingly turned to multinational cooperation: an International Board of Design, including architects from 11 nations, headed by Wallace Harrison of the U.S., the UN's director of planning. These outstanding architects included in alphabetical order: N. D. Bassov (Soviet Union), Gaston Brunfaut (Belgium), Ernest Cormier (Canada), C. E. Le Corbusier (France), Liang Ssu-ch'eng (China), Sven Markelius (Sweden), Oscar Niemeyer (Brazil), Howard Robertson (Britain), G. A. Soilleux (Australia), and Julio Vilamajo (Uruguay).

This distinguished Design Board considered a vast variety of proposed designs—more than four dozen. Finally, it made its choice. More than seventy percent of the site was to be given to flowers, grass, garden, trees. It was to be an oasis of peaceful green amidst the barren stone and cement of the great metropolis.

The space needs of the UN itself were assigned to several contrasting structures, occupying the remainder of the site:

(1) The Secretariat, a great upright slab of a structure, thirty-nine stories—over 500 feet—tall, long, and narrow like the island of Manhattan itself.

(2) The General Assembly building, low and long, located north of the Secretariat.

(3) The Conference Building, linked to both of the above, containing separate chambers for meetings of three vital UN Councils.

(4) The Library, now known as the Dag Hammarskjöld Library, a rectangular structure of six stories at the southern end of the site.

These distinctive and interrelated structures were financed by a sixty-five million dollar loan made to the UN by the U.S. government, with no interest charge, plus two million dollars supplied from the UN's budget. Thus, the total outlay for site, landscaping, and construction was not much over one hundred million dollars. (The cost of a modern aircraft carrier and its war planes may be compared as an illustration of how much more of the world's resources are still lavished on destructive devices rather than on means to maintain peace among nations.)

The start of actual construction was celebrated October 24, 1949, (United Nations Day). The UN General Assembly, in an outdoor meeting, watched the laying of the cornerstone. This symbolic granite block bore the name *UNITED NATIONS* in each of the UN's five official languages: Chinese, English, French, Russian, and Spanish.

This event, as well as all that have followed it at the site, took place surrounded by the territory of the United States, yet legally not within the jurisdiction of the U.S. This seeming paradox is the result of the Headquarters Agreement between the U.S. and the UN. It assures extra-territoriality to the UN site and gives it diplomatic privileges. This means that the legal and judicial authority of the United States does not extend to this site, which is subject only to the jurisdiction of the UN itself.

This protection of extra-territoriality—sometimes called exterritoriality—extends to UN officials while performing their duties, whether or not they are on the site of the Headquarters itself.

The special status of the site is reflected in many ways. It is protected by its own UN security and police force. It has its own local place name and address—simply United Nations, N.Y.—and it has its own postoffice and postage stamps.


WANDERINGS WHILE AWAITING A PERMANENT HOME

It was 1952 before the Secretariat was ready to serve as the working center for some 3000 headquarters officials of the UN, and nearly half that many more assigned to tasks in the field in various other parts of the world.

Before that homecoming to new quarters could occur, the UN staff and the crucial UN meetings had wandered far and wide, using temporary and makeshift facilities.

In 1946, the Security Council met at Hunter College in the Bronx, N.Y. The General Assemblies in 1948 and 1951 met in Paris. Lake Success came into newspaper headlines for an important period because the UN also moved into the unused factory of the Sperry Gyroscope Company, where many a bombsight and other war materials had been manufactured before 1946. During this Lake Success era, additional use was also made of buildings owned by New York City at Flushing Meadows.

In spite of cramped and inconvenient quarters, and in the face of many a disagreement, the work of the UN managed to go on. UN delegates from the growing list of member nations established contacts and customs that set their activities somehow apart from the usual stiff formalities of diplomacy.

The eyes and cameras of the world were focused on the new buildings rising beside the East River. Seldom has a structure or series of structures faced a public more difficult to satisfy. No design could have fulfilled even a fraction of the myriads of expectations and preferences of people who somehow expected something different, even if they could not tell just what.

## THE COMPLETED BUILDINGS–AN EVALUATION

Every building should be judged in terms of its aims. The Board of Design sought to fulfill two major purposes: first, to provide the best possible working space, and second, to produce a group of buildings as beautiful as possible, within the limitations of the requirements of working space and of available funds.

Their aim was not ostentation, pomp, or an awesome display of ornamentation. These buildings were planned from the inside out: the work to be done within dictating the forms chosen to facilitate it.

The official guidebook, *Your United Nations*, points out that, "The buildings are particularly attractive at night when the mellow stone of the Assembly Hall is softly floodlit, the tiny lights of the Conference area shine like stars, the towering mass of the Secretariat building shows some windows bright and others dark, and the long clean lines of the Library stand out, illuminated with clear and penetrating light. The noble purposes of the buildings and their architectural harmony are perhaps never better seen than at the dark and quiet hour."

Yet, day or night, the most memorable and magical views of the UN buildings are likely to be found inside rather than outside. One discovers these, sometimes slowly rather than suddenly, as one moves through passageways, lobbies, meeting halls, lounges, and work areas.

Of all the world's great public structures associated with the tasks of government and international relations, none other has attained its aims more effectively, quietly, and artistically.

The UN's internationality is revealed here in two different ways: on the outside, by simple, almost stark lines that are of our times yet identified with no single, narrow national school or style; on the inside, by a rich variety of decorative treatments and art treasures which are typical of widely differing styles and schools.

It could be said that these structures appear "non-national" without, and "multi-national" within. This over-simplifies, but suggests the contrast and balance achieved in this unique group of structures.


THE SECRETARIAT

This simple rectangular form has been called a glass skyscraper. Its windows, more than 4700 in number, are tinted blue-green to filter out the heat of sunlight. Though glass dominates, aluminum and marble trim are also in evidence on these two great flat sides. They are free from all setbacks, and broken only by four vertical bands placed at pleasing distances between the ground and the flat roof.

Seen from a helicopter overhead, or from top floors of nearby skyscrapers, the slablike shape of the Secretariat is especially striking. It is, indeed, narrow in relation to its width. The windowed sides extend nearly 290 feet. In contrast, the narrow ends, facing north and south, are only one-quarter as wide. Those ends are blind—faced with solid marble quarried in Vermont. They are unbroken by windows. These blind sides emphasize the slablike effect of the whole building.

Of its thirty-nine major floor levels, three are below ground. The wide range of UN activities is reflected in the facilities and even in the engineering of the Secretariat Building. Multistory office buildings have to be strong, but this one was reinforced even more than usual, so it could handle huge archives of correspondence, records, vital papers, and publications. The bulk of such files has been estimated at nearly 14,000 cubic feet.

The simple interior contains the most modern aids to maintain good working conditions. Thus, the huge air-conditioning system allows separate control for each of 4000 office locations.

Here are the working quarters of most of the 3500 UN staff members whose duties keep them at the Headquarters. And here too are the home offices for about 2000 who are in the field, which means at many locations in the world.

Offices of the chief official, the Secretary-General, are near the top of this great staff headquarters in the war for mankind. There too are his conference rooms, the quarters of his secretary and principal aides, and even a residence for his use.

Secretary-General U Thant moved into his high office in November, 1961. His title then was Acting Secretary-General, for he was filling the unexpired term of the preceding Secretary-General, Dag Hammarskjöld, who had been killed in an airplane accident while representing the UN in Africa.

A year later, U Thant was formally appointed Secretary-General for a term running until November, 1966, and at that time, after a period of indecision that caused much worry among supporters of the UN, he accepted a reappointment for another term that is to end in November, 1971.

He reappointed his so-called key deputies to serve with him until that time. His three closest aides are Ralph J. Bunche (U.S.), José Rolz-Bennett (Guatemala), and C. V. Narasimhan (India).

Other aides who, with the foregoing, make up what UN reporters sometimes call the cabinet of the Secretary-General, are Alexei E. Nestorenko (Soviet Union), Bruce Turner (New Zealand), Jiri Nosek (Czechoslovakia), and Issoufou Saidou Djermakoy (Nigeria).

Others in the UN who still head important divisions are D. B. Vaughan (U.S.), head of general services, and Philippe de Seynes (France), head of the economic and social department.

Secretary-General U Thant has retained almost all of the principal aides and department heads who were on hand when he was first appointed in 1962. He has emphasized continuity in his general staff officers.

Even the naming of the national origins of the secretary and his aides calls for a word of caution that illustrates also the character of the headquarters buildings themselves. These UN staff members work solely for the UN itself, and not as representatives of any one nation or group of nations or governments.

The oath taken by every staff member before he goes to work for the UN is specific: "I solemnly swear to exercise . . . the functions entrusted to me as an international civil servant of the United Nations . . . with the interests of the United Nations only in view, and not to seek or accept instructions in regard to the performance of my duties from any Government or other authority external to the Organization [of the UN]."

As one descends by elevator from the level of the Secretary-General's offices, one comes to the Secretariat floors where the work is done through which the UN reaches out into the world with the help of many means of communication: TV, radio, newspapers and other periodicals, books, and so on.

The third floor, near the ground level, is the special domain of the Office of Public Information, the press services and their correspondents. Constant tides of information and comment flow in and out here.

The fourth floor contains a large cafeteria, and banking facilities. Higher still is located a center providing medical and nursing care in case of need.

The labors of the Secretary-General and his staffs of international civil servants are as various as they are vital to the welfare of the world. Some of the subjects that receive attention in the offices of the great upthrusting Secretariat are: disarmament matters, including effects of nuclear radiation; peaceful uses of outer space, extension and simplification of international law; control of narcotics; applications of science and technology, especially to underdeveloped countries; reports on trade conditions; population problems; housing and urbanization; human rights; programs to meet emergency needs of children, especially in underdeveloped countries, and of refugees; and, of course, matters of UN budget and finance, of personnel, and of all field operations.

Outside, in front of the Secretariat, stands a circular fountain built by contributions from children in the United States, Puerto Rico, and the Virgin Islands. Below the fountain lies a pool whose base is patterned in wavy black and white lines. The stones and pebbles from which it is formed were gathered by women and children on the Greek island of Rhodes.

Still further west, near the limits of the UN site, is the great line of flagstaffs, side by side. Here fly the flags of all the member nations. They are placed in alphabetical order, by the names of the countries. Afghanistan's flag flies furthest north (uptown).

These national banners fly every weekday, except during rain, and on weekends if a meeting is in session or if some head of state is visiting the UN buildings. Behind and above these national flags flies the familiar blue flag of the UN itself, on display every day, as if to insist that there can be no halt in the UN's program for mankind.

THE GENERAL ASSEMBLY BUILDING

The low, curving sweep of this limestone and marble structure is in total contrast to the dynamic upthrust of the Secretariat building that lies so near it, in a southwest direction.

It is here, to the northern or uptown end of the General Assembly, that visitors come by the many hundreds of thousands each year to tour the UN headquarters.

The entrance is by seven striking doors, nickel-plated gifts from Canada, bearing bas-relief panels symbolizing the fourfold UN ideals of peace, justice, truth, and fraternity.

Within is a lobby, extending all the way to the roof, 75 feet above.

Three striking objects from far places and periods now make this lobby memorable.

At the east stands one of the most glorious of all Greek statues— a fine reproduction of a figure of a youthful, bearded Zeus, king of the gods, created by an unknown master. Zeus strides along, with arm upraised as if launching a thunderbolt.

At the west, a great gold-plated sphere swings slowly back and forth, suspended from on high. It is a Foucault Pendulum, presented by the Netherlands. Its changes in direction of swing illustrate and prove the rotation of the earth, most of whose nations are members of this UN body.

In the center hangs a full-scale model of *Sputnik,* the Soviet satellite whose launching in 1957, opened the present space age.

The UN guide book recalls that the late Dag Hammarskjöld, second Secretary-General of the UN, said in 1959, regarding the Pendulum and the Sputnik displays, that they show the enormous evolution in science within little more than a century—"on the one side the physical demonstration of the daily rotation of the earth; on the other the first man-made object to circle the globe in outer space."

On the east, or river side lies the long hall-like main lobby, where exhibits of UN activities are displayed. Stairs lead to a public area below. There visitors may make purchases at the UN postal sales center, the bookshop, and the gift shop.

The real impact comes as one enters the impressive General Assembly Hall itself. Its length is 165 feet, its width 115 feet, its height seventy-five feet. Delegates sit below a domed ceiling studded with rings of lights.

The shape of the hall is distinctive and effective. Its sloping walls and a bold simplicity of design, all serve to direct attention toward the rostrum with its black desk from which speakers address the gathering.

Behind that speaker's desk, on a higher level, is the green marble desk with three places: the center for the delegate who serves as President of the Assembly; to his right the Secretary-General's seat;

and at the other side a seat for a deputy or aide of the Secretary-General.

Behind and far above them is hung, like a great target, the familiar emblem of the UN itself—a circular projection of the world, spread out as if seen by an observer high over the North Pole. Around the world thus displayed is wreathed the olive branch, traditional symbol for peace.

Originally this Hall was designed to provide place for some 750 delegates and about 1300 visitors and others. The great increase in UN membership forced changes to be made to give more seats to delegates and alternates.

At present, there are about 160 press seats and more than 300 public seats behind the delegates' seats. Glass-enclosed booths on lower levels of the two side walls, contain interpreters, TV and film cameramen, and broadcasters.

Farther back into the hall are two enormous, swirling, colorful abstract murals based on designs by the late Fernand Léger, a noted French artist. Each fills a wall area between 800 and 1000 square feet. The mural known as "One" lies to the west, in a pattern of white, blue, and yellow. "Two" to the east, is in white, orange, and gray. Both stand out against dark gray backgrounds.

Léger made the mural designs in drawings less than a foot square. They were executed in their present form by Bruce Gregory, an American artist, who had previously worked with the French master.

The importance of the General Assembly is reflected by the provisions to allow the world to follow its sessions. It is the crossroads organ of the UN with the right to discuss all matters that lie within the Charter itself. Each member nation, regardless of size, has one Assembly vote.

From the Assembly are elected all the members of the Economic and Social Council, and some of the members of the Security Council and of the Trusteeship Council. The Assembly may make recommendations to members of the UN on all subjects other than those that are being dealt with by the Security Council.

On the ground level, in the south lobby of this building, is dis-

played the largest of UN murals. It was painted in the mid-1950s by Candido Portinari, a Brazilian, who worked on panels of cedar. On the one side is a dark, somber picture of "War"; on the other, in serene tones, "Peace" interprets the state of the world toward which the UN labors.

The General Assembly Building as a whole brings together construction materials, handiwork, and art objects from many nations. Its exterior stone has come from England, Italy, and Israel. The rich woods of its interior grew in Belgium, Canada, Cuba, Guatemala, Norway, and the Philippines. Much of its floor covering was woven in Scotland.

The languages in which the great problems of the world may be discussed at Assembly sessions are also varied. Five official languages are in use: Chinese, English, French, Russian, and Spanish. A speech made in any one of these is given simultaneous translation into the other four. Delegates can dial in to the desired language on their headphones.

This advanced system of instant translation is used not only in the Assembly but also in all Council chambers.

THE CONFERENCE BUILDING

The structure containing the Council meeting halls is the Conference Building. Seen from a passing ship, this UN structure nearest the East River is a long, low, unpretentious building. It seems to link the base of the Secretariat with the southern end of the Assembly Building.

The Conference Building does serve as such a link. An ample and impressive corridor leads from the Secretariat, via the Conference Building, to the Assembly Building.

The Conference Building extends 400 feet from north to south. Its back windows face Franklin D. Roosevelt Drive, the high-speed road along the East River shore. Its depth from east to west is 180 feet, and it stands 55 feet high, dwarfed by the upreaching Secretariat beside it. Its unassuming exterior gives no hint of the variety and verve of the three distinctive meeting halls within: the chambers of the (1) Security, (2) Economic and Social, and (3) Trustee-ship Councils.

They are all identical in dimensions, although they differ in decoration, coloring, and over-all effect, as well as the tasks they are intended to serve. Each is fitted into a length of 135 feet, front to back; seventy-two feet side to side; and twenty-four feet from floor to top. Each is designed to provide ample seating and working space for the delegates of the Council assigned to it. Seats are supplied also for more than 100 journalists and about 400 visitors.

Those most familiar with the actual operations of the UN rank the Security Council first in importance. Its Council chamber is surely one of the most impressive and beautiful sights in the head-quarters. Arnstein Arenberg, a Norwegian, designed it, and Norway supplied the decorations and materials to realize this conception.

Around a great curved table sit the delegates and aides of the eleven nations making up the Security Council. Five are permanent members: the United States, the Soviet Union, the United King-dom, France, and Nationalist China. To these are added by elec-tion six non-permanent member nations who serve two-year terms.

Security Council decisions require the votes of seven members, and if the question concerns more than a mere matter of procedure, then those votes must include all the five permanent members.

Any one of the five principal and permanent powers may thus withhold its approval, and so exercise a veto, though all ten other Council members are in favor. Many an intensely debated proposal has thus been blocked, especially by refusal of the representative of the Soviet Union to cast a favoring vote.

Looming over the Security Council seats is a great wall mural by the Norwegian artist, Per Krohg. It symbolizes war versus peace—the ills of the old world that the UN was organized to reform, and the hope of the better world to be attained. It is a rich and complex mural, separated into panels, suggesting the conflicting forces by its contrasting colors and human forms.

Great windows frame the mural on both sides and add to the feeling of space and dignity. As in all three of these chambers, tele-vision cameras and radio reporters are here provided with glassed-in accommodations in the side walls overlooking the Council area. Marble wall areas and inlaid wooden doors contribute to the total effect.

The Economic and Social Council chamber was designed by a Swede, Sven Markelius. Woodwork and carpeting also came from Sweden. From its white marble floor below, to its suspended ceiling overhead, it too is an impressive and unusual enclosure.

The lofty windows at the far end of the room are made radiant by an enormous curtain, the largest of its kind, woven in Sweden especially for this purpose. It weighs more than 750 pounds, and when extended fully covers an area of about 1800 square feet. Simplicity and vigor are united in its richly blended colors.

The third of the great chambers, that of the Trusteeship Council, embodies the art of the third Scandinavian country—Denmark. Finn Juhl created the design, and the sculptor Henrik Starche executed the heroic wooden statue called *Mankind and Hope*. It shows a child whose lifted arms betoken humanity's yearning for a better world. In hue and pattern, the decorations of the chamber suggest the effect of bamboo, though woodwork and curtains and other materials are Danish rather than tropical in origin.

A variety of other and smaller committee and conference rooms are provided also, as well as the dining room for delegates, and many other fine facilities for making the daily routines more pleasant and life more livable for those who use the great headquarters.

The Conference Building offers unusual art experiences in rich variety, often where one would not expect. For example, there are the outstanding Zanetti murals on the curved wall of the third floor lobby of the Conference Building, the passageway between the Secretariat and the Assembly Building. Spanish-born, Italian-trained, and Dominican by adoption, José Vale Zanetti had worked and been exhibited widely in Latin America. In this historic hallway he painted in powerful forms and penetrating colors his vision of human progress from brutality and superstition toward peace and dignity.

Zanetti worked a total of fifteen months on the murals, which he painted directly on the cloth-covered wall of the lobby. He pictured the horrors of modern war: concentration camps, bombings, whole-sale destruction; and set over against them the labors of reconstruction, reconciliation, and international cooperation.

For many visitors to the Headquarters, the most powerful single impression is made by the great hall of the General Assembly itself.

## THE UN LIBRARY

The Dag Hammarskjöld Library at the south end of the UN is an enlargement and rebuilding of the original UN Library, thanks to a grant of more than $6 million from the Ford Foundation.

The new Library provides space for some 400,000 books, double the former capacity, as well as about 1500 periodicals and enormous numbers of maps, charts, and reference works of all types. Principal emphasis is on international relations, political science, history, geography, economics, and related subjects.

Much of the material here is difficult or impossible to find in any other library in the world.

The Library, constructed of glass, aluminum, and white marble, has a penthouse on top of its six stories. Beside the bookshelves and reading rooms, the Library includes an auditorium of moderate size, in shape somewhat like a classical Greek theater.

Modern abstract art in styles favored by the late Secretary-General Hammarskjöld was chosen to highlight selected areas of the Library. In the penthouse lounge, on a curved wall nearest First Avenue, is a bold abstract design in oils on canvas, painted by Bo Beskow, a well-known Swedish artist.

The same artist, in a quieter, more contemplative style, painted the abstract fresco for the so-called Meditation Room that lies at the west of the public lobby of the General Assembly Building. This unique room with tapered walls is a kind of chapel dedicated to silence "where only thoughts should speak."

Like an altar in the center of this strange cell of silence, stands a huge block of Swedish iron ore, 12,000 pounds in weight. It, too, speaks without words, of utter silence and unchanging endurance.

In conception and design, the Meditation Room reflects the unusual mind of Hammerskjöld himself, a man of great complexity.

Still another reflection of his preferences in art stands on a wall opposite a terrazzo stairway that descends from the principal lobby of the Library to the auditorium underneath. This is a severe rectilinear geometrical abstraction by Fritz Glarner, a Swiss-Italian-born artist, active in the United States during more than thirty years. His work was followed with favor by Hammarskjöld while the latter served as Secretary-General.

## FURNISHED BY THE WORLD

The UN Headquarters contain more works of art than can be seen in a short visit or can be described in these pages. At most we can sample a few treasures, and emphasize the extent to which good taste and restraint have preserved harmony among these varied styles and traditions.

Contributions have come from scores of nations: not every gift offered could be accepted and displayed. Each proposed addition is now studied by the advisory art committee appointed by the Secretary-General. The results must be judged in the buildings themselves and in the gardens and vistas outside.

Here are some of the contributions that have added their glories to the UN Headquarters.

From Ecuador came great rugs, whose patterns were created by primitive Jivaro Indians, as interpreted by Olga A. Fisch, a modern Hungarian-Ecuadorian designer. Funds for some of these rugs came from a group of American women. These rugs are displayed in the General Assembly and also in the area between it and the Conference Building. Other superb rugs come from India, Iran, and Turkey, woven in their respective traditional styles.

From Ghana, Africa, an imposing *kente* tapestry of silk in various colors was sent and hung in the delegates' lobby of the General Assembly Building.

A wooden statue of peace, artist unknown, comes from Indonesia and is exhibited in the southwest foyer of the General Assembly Building.

An outdoor pagoda of cypress wood, containing a great peace bell, cast from melted coins contributed by the Japanese people, is shown on a marble pedestal beside the Secretariat.

Two mosaics, one from Morocco and one from Tunisia, are shown in the area between the General Assembly and the Conference Buildings.


## A ROLL CALL OF EMINENT ARTISTS

Art works signed by significant artists of many nations are also among the treasures that enrich the UN Headquarters. Here again only a sampling can be offered. The nations with which they are identified are listed to stress the international range.

*Stewart Armfield—England*. His painting, *Vortex,* was hung near the door to the Secretary-General's office in the Secretariat.

*Antun Augustincic—Yugoslavia*. His bronze equestrian statue *Mir* (Peace) looms impressively in the north garden. It stands sixteen feet high, atop a marble base twenty-six feet tall.

*A. R. Chugtai—Belgium*. Several of his haunting paintings were hung at the entry to the delegates' dining room.

*Peter Colfs—Belgium*. His prize-winning design was woven into the enormous Mechlin tapestry, more than twenty-eight by forty-three feet, which is hung on the north wall of the delegates' lobby. More than a dozen master weavers worked over three years to complete this representation of the concepts of equality, well-being, and peace.

*M. Cormier—Canada*. He designed the panels of nickel-bronze at the north portal of the General Assembly Building.

*Robert Cronbach—U.S.* His abstract sculpture was hung in the Meditation Room. To some it may suggest a ship sailing into the silences. To others it is a subtle abstract design.

*Harald Dal—Norway*. His portrait painting of Trygve Lie, the first UN Secretary-General, was hung in the Secretary-General's office.

*Raoul Dufy—France*. The light, joyful style of the late French painter is well known in the art world. His watercolor of the UN Headquarters is part of the valuable and growing collection of artworks donated to the United Nations Children's Fund (UNICEF). UNICEF's fund-raising by the sale of fine and colorful holiday greeting cards is well known and widely supported.

*Hans Erni—Switzerland and France.* His painting, *Brothers,* was another of many gifts to the UNICEF collection.

*Hsin-Yu—Nationalist China.* His delicate *Marine Scene,* a water color, and his *Landscape,* in ink and brush, were hung in the dining room of the Conference Building.

*Rikhardour Johnson—Iceland.* His woodcarving, a gavel made from the birch of his native land, became a showpiece of the chamber of the General Assembly's first, or political, committee.

*Ezio Martinelli—U.S.* His "prickly" abstract sculpture of aluminum was hung on the east wall, General Assembly Building.

*Henri Matisse—France.* One of the giants of modern art. His simple cutout, *Torch of Hope,* is part of the UNICEF collection.

*Joan Miró—Spain and France.* His delightful and deceptively naive *Children and Birds* was a gift to the UNICEF collection.

*Pablo Picasso—Spain and France.* Most influential among living artists. His painting, *Woman on the Ladder,* was re-created as a tapestry, signature and all, by Marie Cuttali. It was hung in the southern delegates hall, chamber of the Security Council.

*C. T. Pledge—England.* His designs of plants, birds, and other animals are in the fine oak paneling of Committee Room No. 8, the General Assembly Building.

*José de Rivera—U.S.* His arching and flowing abstract sculpture was hung on the wall of the Secretary-General's office.

*Rufino Tamayo—Mexico.* His spirited composition, *Poetry on the Wing,* was a gift to the UNICEF collection.

*Evgeny V. Vuyetich—Soviet Union.* His powerful and realistic statue, *Let Us Beat Our Swords Into Plowshares,* stands in the garden north of the major building complex. Before it was presented to the UN it had won the highest award at the Brussels International Exposition in 1958.

AND MANY MORE . . .

Even a complete inventory of the UN Headquarters in Manhattan would not truly cover this subject. These structures are also the home offices for many associated agencies and operations widely scattered in the world. Over a dozen such specialized agencies have their own headquarters elsewhere. (A directory in the Appendix lists them on p. 275.)

Each of these specialized agencies serves to execute projects of the UNDP, which stands for United Nations Development Program, centered at the UN Headquarters. These agencies also conduct their own surveys and projects related to their development. Each works with the UN under special agreements. Each is a part of the program of peace maintenance and world development for which the UN was formed. If, in this world of great-power armaments and animosities, the UN does not suffice to restore and maintain peace, the work of all these various agencies will suffer—and the last best hope of mankind will be destroyed.

END OF A CYCLE

Our cycle of great structures began with the ziggurats of Mesopotamia and the Tower of Babel—that powerful symbol of disunity and discord. We close with the UN building, dedicated to unity and concord among the nations of the world.

Will this latest effort to unite and pacify the world fail, as did the ineffectual League of Nations and other gestures toward international agreement against war? Will all these steps toward communication, conference, and cooperation be frustrated?

These questions cannot be dodged, no matter which way we turn today. Never have the possibilities for better life in the world been more promising; never has the price of failure been more dreadful.

"The wonderful creations of men . . . are in danger of obliteration or destruction in this second half of the 20th century, in the shadow of the hydrogen bomb."

Those words were spoken by U Thant as he opened the 17th annual exhibit of the Art Club of the UN, an exhibit composed of more than 150 pictures and sculptures for the benefit of UNICEF. Secretary-General U Thant was speaking to over 300 persons gathered in the UN's public lobby. He was addressing also the great world outside.

The answers to these overwhelming questions are being shaped, and will yet be shaped, by human decisions and actions. The hour is dreadfully late, but it is not midnight—not quite.

The great structures of the world, and the great structure of the world itself, are all in danger. Like markers seeking to point the path to survival, the UN structures loom up. For the final choice remains: one world—or none!

# APPENDIX

Operations and agencies of the United Nations

FAO—Food and Agriculture Organization: Vialle delle Terme di Caracalla, Rome, Italy

GATT—General Agreement on Tariffs and Trade: Geneva Switzerland

IAEA—International Atomic Energy Agency: Kaerntnerring 11, Vienna, Austria

IBRD—International Bank for Reconstruction and Development: Washington, D.C.

ICAO—International Civil Aviation Organization: International Aviation Building, Montreal, Quebec, Canada

IDA—International Development Association: Washington, D.C.

IFC—International Finance Corporation: Washington, D.C.

ILO—International Labor Organization: 154, Rue Lausanne, Geneva, Switzerland

ITU—International Telecommunication Union: Place des Nations, Geneva, Switzerland

IMCO—Inter-Governmental Maritime Consultative Organization: Chancery House, Chancery Lane, London, WC 2, England

UNESCO—United Nations Educational, Scientific and Cultural Organization: UNESCO House, Place de Fontenoy, Paris 7e, France

UPU—Universal Postal Union: Schlosshaldenstrasse 46, Berne, Switzerland

WHO—World Health Organization: Avenue Appia, Geneva, Switzerland

WMO—World Meteorological Organization: Avenue Giuseppe Motta, Geneva, Switzerland

BOOKS FOR FURTHER READING

## MAN'S MARCH TO GREAT STRUCTURES

Clark, Grahame: *World Prehistory: An Outline*. Cambridge, Cambridge
  University Press, 1961.

Dobzhansky, Theodosius: *Mankind Evolving*. New Haven, Yale University
  Press, 1962.

Hawkes, Jacquetta: *Prehistory*, vol. 1, part 1. New York, The New American Library, 1963.

————— (ed.): *World of the Past*. New York, Alfred A. Knopf, 1963, 2 vols.

## THE ZIGGURATS AND THE TOWER OF BABEL

Boscawen, W. St. Chad: *The First of Empires*. New York, Harper and Row.

Champdor, Albert: *Babylon*. London, Dufour, 1958.

Childe, V. Gordon: *Man Makes Himself*. New York, The New American
  Library, 1951.

Cottrell, Leonard: *The Anvil of Civilization*. New York, The New American
  Library, 1957.

—————: *The Quest of Sumer*. New York, G.P. Putnam's Sons, 1965.

Maspero, Gaston: *The Dawn of Civilization*. London, Macmillan, 1922.

Parrot, André: *Babylon and the Old Testament*. New York, Philosophical
  Library, 1958.

—————: *Nineveh and the Old Testament*. New York, Philosophical Library,
  1956.

—————: *Nineveh and Babylon*. London: Thames & Hudson, 1961.

Roux, Georges: *Ancient Iraq*. Cleveland, The World Publishing Co., 1965.

Saggs, H. W. F.: *The Greatness That Was Babylon*. New York, Hawthorn
  Books, 1962.

## THE PYRAMIDS OF EGYPT

Cottrell, Leonard: *The Mountains of Pharaoh*. New York: Holt, Rinehart
  & Winston, 1956.

—————: *Life Under the Pharaohs*. New York, Holt, Rinehart & Winston,
  1960.

Edwards, I. E. S.: *The Pyramids of Egypt*. Baltimore, Maryland, Penguin Books, 1961.

Fakhry, Ahmed: *The Pyramids*. Chicago, University of Chicago Press, 1961.

## THE PARTHENON ON THE ACROPOLIS

Durant, Will: *Our Oriental Heritage,* vol. 1 of *The Story of Civilization*. New York, Simon and Schuster, 1935.

McNeill, William H.: *The Rise of the West*. New York, The New American Library, 1965.

Powers, H. H.: *The Hill of Athena*. New York, Macmillan, 1924.

Quennell, Majorie and C. H. B.: *Everyday Things in Ancient Greece*. New York, G. P. Putnam's Sons, 1954.

Rodenwaldt, Gerhart: *The Acropolis*. London, Oxford University Press, 1957.

## THE GREAT WALL OF CHINA

Clark, Grover: *The Great Wall Crumbles*. New York, Macmillan, 1935.

Geil, William E.: *The Great Wall of China*. New York, Sturgis & Walton Co., 1909.

Grousset, Rene: *The Rise and Splendor of the Chinese Empire*. Berkeley, Calif., University of California Press, 1953.

Miller, J. A.: *Master Builders of Sixty Centuries*. New York, Appleton-Century, 1938.

Silverberg, Robert: *The Great Wall of China*. Philadelphia, Chilton Books, 1965.

Wells, H. G.: *The Outline of History*. Garden City, N.Y., Doubleday, 1956.

## THE COLOSSEUM OF ROME

Durant, Will: *Caesar and Christ,* vol. 3 of *The Story of Civilization*. New York, Simon and Schuster, 1944.

————: *The Age of Faith,* vol. 4 of *The Story of Civilization*. New York, Simon and Schuster, 1950.

Field, W. T.: *Rome, the Eternal City*. London, Hamilton, 1927.

## THE CHURCH OF SANTA SOPHIA

Beckwith, John: *The Art of Constantinople*. New York, New York Graphic Press (Phaidon), 1961.

Gibbon, Edward: *The Decline and Fall of the Roman Empire*. New York, Modern Library, 1960.

Lewis, Bernard: *Istanbul and the Civilization of the Ottoman Empire.* Norman, Okla., University of Oklahoma Press, 1963.

Millon, Henry A. and Frazer, Alfred: *Key Monuments of the History of Architecture.* New York, Abrams, 1964.

Muller, Herbert J.: *The Uses of the Past.* New York, The New American Library, 1954.

Rice, David T.: *Constantinople: From Byzantium to Istanbul.* New York, Stein and Day, 1965.

## MACHU PICCHU

Baudin, Louis: *Daily Life in Peru Under the Last Incas.* New York, Macmillan, 1962.

Bingham, Hiram: *Lost City of the Incas.* New York, Atheneum, 1963.

Brundage, Burr C.: *Empire of the Inca.* Norman, Okla., University of Oklahoma Press, 1963.

Bushnell, Geoffrey H. S.: *Peru.* New York, Praeger, 1957.

Flornoy, Bertrand: *The World of the Inca.* New York, Vanguard, 1956.

Masters, Robert V.: *Peru in Pictures.* New York, Sterling Press, 1965.

Von Hagen, Victor W.: *Realm of the Incas.* New York, The New American Library, 1957.

————: *Ancient Sun Kingdoms of the Americas.* Cleveland, The World Publishing Co., 1961.

## THE TAJ MAHAL

Chevrillon, André: "The Taj Mahal in Agra" in *Turrets, Towers, and Temples,* ed. by E. Singleton. New York, Dodd, Mead & Co., 1898.

Fabri, Charles: *An Introduction to Indian Architecture.* New York, Asia Publishing House, 1963.

## THE PANAMA CANAL

Lee, William Storrs: *The Strength to Move a Mountain.* New York: G. P. Putnam's Sons, 1958.

————: *Canal Across a Continent,* London: G. G. Harrap & Co., 1961.

## THE EMPIRE STATE BUILDING

Barr, George: *A Young Scientist Looks at Skyscrapers.* New York, McGraw-Hill, 1963.

Gies, Joseph: *Wonders of the Modern World.* New York, Crowell, 1966.

Shultz, Earle and Simmons, Walter: *Offices in the Sky*. Indianapolis, Bobbs-Merrill, 1959.

## THE GRAND COULEE DAM

U.S. Department of the Interior: *The Story of the Columbia Basin Project*. (Booklet.) Washington, D.C., U.S. Government Printing Office, 1964.

## THE NETHERLANDS RECLAMATION PROJECTS

Geyl, Pieter: *Revolt of the Netherlands, 1555–1609*. London, Benn, 1966.

Groenman, Sjoerd: *Land Out of the Sea: The Conquest of the Zuyder Zee*. Meppel, The Netherlands, A. Roelofs Van Goor, 1957.

Pingaud, Bernard: *Holland*. New York, Viking Press, 1962.

Spieker, Eugene: *The Netherlands*. Munich, Germany, W. Andermann Verlag, 1958.

## THE UNITED NATIONS

Baal-Teshuva, Jacob: *Art Treasures of the United Nations*. New York, Yoseloff, 1964.

Rubin, Jacob A.: *A Pictorial History of the United Nations*. New York, Yoseloff, 1963.

# WORKS CITED IN TEXT

1. Cottrell, Leonard: *The Anvil of Civilization*. New York, New American Library, 1957.

2. Durant, Will: *Our Oriental Heritage,* vol. 1 of *The Story of Civilization*. New York, Simon and Schuster, 1935.

3. Edwards, I. E. S.: *The Pyramids of Egypt*. Baltimore, Maryland, Penguin Books, 1961.

4. Rodenwaldt, Gerhart: *The Acropolis*. London, Oxford University Press, 1957.

5. Beckwith, John: *The Art of Constantinople*. New York, New York Graphic Press (Phaidon), 1961.

6. Geil, William E.: *The Great Wall of China*. New York, Sturgis & Walton Co., 1909.

7. Abramson, Samuel and Postal, Bernard: *The Landmarks of a People*. New York, Hill & Wang, 1962.

8. Field, W. T.: *Rome, the Eternal City*. London, Hamilton, 1927.

9. *The Cambridge Ancient History,* vol. II. New York, Macmillan, 1923–1929.

10. Field, W. T.: *Op. cit.*

11. Gibbon, Edward: *The Decline and Fall of the Roman Empire*. New York, Modern Library, 1960.

12. Field, W. T.: *Op. cit.*

13. Gibbon, Edward: *Op. cit.*

14. Procopius: *Buildings,* vol. 7. The Loeb Library, Cambridge, Harvard University Press, 1940.

15. Gibbon, Edward: *Op. cit.*

16. Fabri, Charles: *An Introduction to Indian Architecture*. New York, Asia Publishing House, 1963.

17. Durant, Will: *Op. cit.*

# INDEX

**COMMITTEE FOR TECHNICAL EDUCATION**